Folk Sto1
from the
Yorkshire Dales

Peter N. Walker is the author of a number of highly successful thrillers and of *Murders and Mysteries from the Yorkshire Dales*. As Nicholas Rhea, he has written *Portrait of the North York Moors* in addition to the popular 'Constable' series.

He recently retired as an Inspector with the North Yorkshire Police to concentrate on his writing. He is married with four adult children and lives in Ampleforth.

as Nicholas Rhea
Constable on the Hill
Constable on the Prowl
Constable Around the Village
Constable Across the Moors
Constable in the Dale
Constable by the Sea
Constable Along the Lane
Constable Through the
  Meadow
Constable in Disguise
Constable Among the Heather
Portrait of the North York
  Moors

as Peter N. Walker
Murders and Mysteries from
  the North Yorks Moors
Folk Tales from the north
  York Moors
Murders and Mysteries from
  the Yorkshire Dales
Carnaby and the Hijackers
Carnaby and the Gaolbreakers
Carnaby and the Assassins
Carnaby and the Conspirators
Carnaby and the Saboteurs
Fatal Accident
Panda One on Duty
Special Duty
Carnaby and the Eliminators
Identification Parade
Carnaby and the
  Demonstrators

Panda One Investigates
Carnaby and the Infiltrators
The Dovingsby Death
Carnaby and the
  Kidnappers
The MacIntyre Plot
Missing from Home
Witchcraft for Panda One
Target Criminal
Carnaby and the
  Counterfeiters
The Carlton Plot
Siege for Panda One
Teenage Cop
Carnaby and the
  Campaigners
Robber in a Mole Trap

as Christopher Coram
A Call to Danger
A Call to Die
Death in Ptarmigan Forest
Death on the Motorway
Murder by the Lake
Murder beneath the Trees
Prisoner on the Dam
Prisoner on the Run

as Tom Ferris
Espionage for a Lady

as Andrew Arncliffe
Murder after the Holiday

Folk Stories
from the
Yorkshire Dales

PETER N. WALKER

ROBERT HALE · LONDON

ISBN 0 7090 4486 0

Robert Hale Limited
Clerkenwell House
Clerkenwell Green
London EC1R 0HT

Photoset in Palatino in North Wales by
Derek Doyle & Associates, Mold, Clwyd.
Printed in great Britain by
St Edmundsbury Press Limited, Bury St Edmunds, Suffolk.
Bound by WBC Bookbinders Limited.

Contents

Author's Preface

The area of northern England known as the Yorkshire
Dales includes a huge tract of spectacular countryside. It is
rich with historical associations and its people are of a
strong and sturdy nature, hardly the type to believe in
fairies, giants and mythical creatures.

Nonetheless, the Dales do provide a wealth of folk
stories, some based on historical events and others coming
either from the imagination or from the memories of those
who lived here a long, long time ago. The origins of some
tales are of such antiquity that they cannot be traced and
may even date to the earliest inhabitants of this beautiful
part of England.

I have not included ghost stories, although accounts of
some spectres are, of necessity, contained within these
pages because they are within the scope of folklore rather
than a mere ghostly yarn.

As with all collections of folk stories, I have taken the
liberty of using the so-called 'novelist's licence' to tell the
stories in my own way. Although a tale might not be the
version known to particular readers, change is an essential
part of folklore. Folk stories do change and that is their
strength – without change, many would never survive.

It is hoped that this modest collection will encourage
visits to the locations and so ensure the preservation of
these ancient tales.

Peter N. Walker

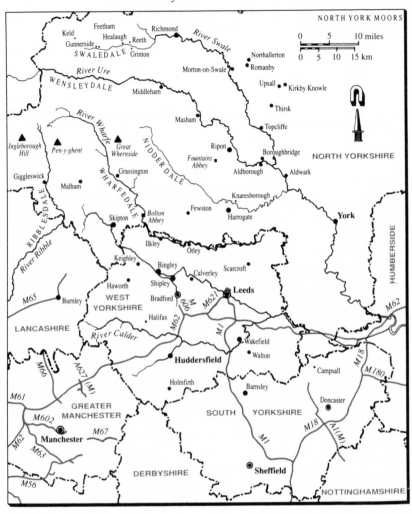

1 Appletreewick –

The Tale of Troller's Gill

Appletreewick is a small but pretty Dales village with a set of stocks and two picturesque inns among beautiful old stone houses which line the short but steep main street. Although it enjoys a beautiful setting in the upper reaches of Wharfedale, it does lie on the edge of wild and elevated open moorland. Being one of the oldest settlements in the area, it is not surprising that the village and its environs are rich with enduring folk stories. There are age-old tales of mythical creatures, fairies, trolls and ghosts, many of which are still told.

To the north are the open heatherclad reaches of the curiously named Appletreewick Pasture, while Barden Fell and Barden Moor lie to the south, these two lofty areas being divided by the River Wharfe as it flows from the Pennine fells. On a summit to the north of Barden Fell is an odd but very prominent group of rocks known as Swart Simon or Simon's Seat (1590 ft/484 metres above sea level). It is visible from a great distance and commands extensive views. Some authorities suggest that this might be where the druids practised their religious rites, and that it is named after one of them, Simon Magnus.

A much more interesting tale is that many years ago, a shepherd called Simon found a baby boy who had been abandoned among these rocks. The old shepherd was unmarried and had no idea how to care for a baby, but he gathered up the infant, a mere six months old, and took him to his own modest shelter. He told his story to a friend who was married and asked his advice. After some discussion, it was decided that all the shepherds of the district should meet to determine the best method of dealing with the foundling. They decided they would all rear him; the family of each shepherd would contribute to a common fund and all would take turns in caring for him; in that way, the child was reared by all. He was also called Simon after the man who found him, and became known as Simon Amang 'Em (Simon Among Them). According to Halliwell Sutcliffe, that delightful chronicler of the Dales, the surname *Amangham* still exists. (See also 'Sessay'.) This story tells of the first holder of that name.

Simon Amang 'Em is commemorated in Little Simon's Seat which is nearby, while Lord's Seat is at a further short distance. This might be in memory of some past Lord of the Manor. Around here, the rocks have assumed some curious shapes due to centuries of weathering and the open moors are replete with curlews, skylarks and grouse.

In bygone times, the village hosted a large three-day fair which was noted for its sheep, horses and horned beasts. It was the most important fair in the area.

Many of the cattle had been driven from Scotland and the sheep were exposed for sale on a hillside known locally as Sheep Fair Hill. As the livestock fair was in progress, the street was lined with stalls selling a whole range of country fare. This included clothing, shoes, trinkets, fruit and vegetables, and a local speciality which was onions. Their importance as food for winter led to them being known as 'winter beef'.

The Onion Fair, called Apple'rick or Aptrick Onion Fair by the local people, came to an end in the last century, but was still talked about for years afterwards. Onions formed a large portion of the dalesman's diet, especially in the winter months as the old name suggests, and Onion Lane reminds us of the venue of that old fair. Although the name-plate for Onion Lane was removed very recently, its site remains and is opposite Mock Beggar Hall.

Even now, the name of 'Aptrick Fair' revives stories of dancing in High Hall and feasting after the fair was over. Superb feasts with music and dancing were held in all the available village buildings and even Shakespearian plays, very popular with the Dales people, were held in the hall of the High Hall by courtesy of the Craven family.

Appletreewick can be reached from several directions; one is by a minor road leading from the B6160 which follows the splendid route of the Wharfe from Bolton Abbey to Kettlewell.

Turn off the B6160 at either Burnsall Bridge or near the remains of Barden Tower (see later for the story of the Shepherd Lord who lived at Barden Tower). Another breathtaking route is from the Pateley Bridge to Grassington road (B6265) at a point between Dibbles Bridge and Stump Cross Caverns. Head south along the so-called New Road which leads via Hazler Lane into Appletreewick.

Appletreewick dates to the time of the Danish invasion of the Dales and it remained in the hands of the Danes until the time of William the Conqueror. Later, it passed into the ownership of Bolton Priory and its links with the past have left the village with some interesting old buildings and several halls. For such a tiny place, there is a preponderance of halls! They include Low Hall, a seventeenth-century house with a huge stone trough and once the home of the Sedgwicks, Monks Hall standing on the site of a grange for the canons of Bolton Priory, Hall Wells near the site of the former village well, Mock Beggar Hall and High Hall with a minstrel gallery over the dining-room, and a huge studded door. This was home of the Cravens and was undergoing building work when I arrived.

Little over a mile away, near the hamlet of Skyreholme which once housed a water-powered paper mill, is the splendid Parcevall Hall with its magnificent sixteen acres of gardens. These are open to the public from Easter until the end of October.

In former times, the Hall was occupied by a local magistrate who had cells built to accommodate offenders as they awaited trial, and the hall is said to have sheltered the highwayman Swift Nick Nevison on occasions when he was in danger. He was not held here as a prisoner, but was welcomed as a friend; some stories say that Dick Turpin was the highwayman who sheltered here, but it was almost certainly Nevison, a man of high breeding known by the local gentry.

In times gone by, it was claimed that one of the stables at

Parcevall Hall was haunted; horses which spent the night there were terrified, shivering as they entered and foaming at the mouth by next morning. It was hinted that some unknown but terrible tragedy had occurred within that stable but the details have been obscured by the passage of time. At one end of the hall was a strange bride-house – the family gave this to the heir and his new wife, so that they could be close to their true home as the children matured. Male children were always wanted so that the family line would continue.

Today, this beautiful hall is a retreat house and conference centre for the Bradford Diocese of the Church of England. Spellings of its name vary from the present Parcevall to Parsible or Parsifal via Percival, the precise pronunciation often varying with local speech. One account suggests it was originally called Parson's Hall after the Reverend Haye who lived there.

The gardens in this unusual moorland setting are renowned for their variety of plants, shrubs and trees which are seldom found so far to the north, or at such an elevation.

Appletreewick, which lies within the Yorkshire Dales National Park, also boasts a variety of names such as Aptrick, Apterick, Apteruck and others, although its correct name is really Appletrewick (with one 'e'). It boasts a tiny church of St John the Baptist which bears the misleading date 1635 above the door. This building was originally a pair of houses with supposed links with one of the famous families of this village, the Cravens, hence its cottage-like appearance.

Theirs is a romantic story which has all the elements of a legend, except that this is true. It begins with a humble child of this village, for it was his sense of adventure combined with his business acumen which laid the foundations of the amazing Craven dynasty. Within only one generation, and from peasant origins, they were to marry into the royal family.

Because of his life and career, that brave young Craven is constantly compared with Dick Whittington, sometimes being referred to as the Dick Whittington of the Dales. He was to become Sir William Craven and it is said that the cottage in which he was born in 1548 was one of the pair later converted into the tiny parish church of St John the Baptist. That conversion occurred in 1897-98.

This is his story.

In the sixteenth century, the young William Craven, aged thirteen and born to very lowly parents, left home in Appletreewick to seek his fortune. The parish authorities encouraged him and it is said he obtained lifts or travelled by carrier's cart until he arrived in London. There he became a tailor's boy, but his honesty gained the trust of his master, Robert Hulson, and the young Craven made a success of his menial job. By the time he was twenty-one, he had been admitted to the membership of the Merchant Taylor's Guild and through sheer hard work, he became a noted businessman in London. Eventually, he bought a splendid mansion and became Warden of the Mercers Company as well as Alderman of the City of London.

He was one of the last Sheriffs under Queen Elizabeth I; he was knighted by King James I and in 1611 became Lord Mayor of London. In spite of his enormous success in London, he always remembered his Dales childhood and returned whenever he could, loving to walk beside the Wharfe and to explore the fells. He rebuilt High Hall in Appletreewick and it became his home. It is probable that he created the minstrel gallery earlier referred to. He lavished generous amounts of cash upon local hospitals and schools, founding a Grammar School at Burnsall in 1602 and helping to found a college at Ripon. He was founder of the family which became the Earls of Craven and his son, the second William Craven, lived a highly adventurous and romantic life, eventually marrying Elizabeth, the sister of Charles I.

She was a queen, for she was the widow of the King of Bohemia. It was this William Craven who became the first Baron Craven, the honour being bestowed by this Elizabeth's nephew, Charles II.

The Craven name is perpetuated in an area of the high Dales known as the Craven District. Names like the Craven Herald, Craven Heifer Inn, Craven Dales and Craven District Council are part of everyday life. Skipton is sometimes called Skipton-in-Craven and although the local authority imposes its own boundaries, the original area known simply as Craven included parts of Wharfedale down to Ilkley, Airedale as far as Bingley and portions of upper Ribblesdale, plus Skipton.

That famous Yorkshire benefactor is buried in London but his generous spirit lives on in this lovely countryside.

With stories like this (and there are many), it is evident that the local landscape is rich with historical associations and romance. Over the centuries, these have combined to produce the inevitable legends and myths.

The focal point for some enduring folk tales is a remote half-mile stretch of moorland stream where it roars through a narrow limestone gorge. The stream is Skyreholme Beck which rises on the moors to the north-east of Appletreewick. Several minor gills merge as they head towards the Wharfe, eventually becoming Skyreholme Beck before passing the grounds of Parcevall Hall on their journey to join the Wharfe about a mile away.

Those small gills unite to the north of this astonishing fissure in the rocks; it is only a few yards (metres) wide at its broadest part, but it is at least sixty feet (18.25 metres) deep – or even more. Those waters enter this chasm and roar along its rock-strewn floor to emerge as Skyreholme Beck. There is the constant roar of water even in the summer, but when the waters are high and fast running after the winter snows and rains, the noise and spectacle can be quite menacing. Old accounts said the chasm was disconcerting in the daytime, but terrifying after nightfall. That it continues to exude a strange atmosphere is seldom denied and to be there during a thunderstorm is, I am assured, a memorable experience!

There is little wonder the chasm has given rise to stories of trolls which cast rocks on to the unwary who pass beneath, or to tales of fairies which were said to live in the surrounding fells. Not surprisingly, the locality has also produced several accounts of ghosts.

The ghost of Thomas Preston, an evil man in life and disliked by most, was said to noisily haunt Low Hall in the village, until his ghost was exorcised to dwell for evermore in a grave now known as Preston's Well in Dibb Gill. Another spectre haunted the lane outside Appletreewick, cursed to wander for ever for defrauding a neighbour of some land.

But the enduring story of the gill is about a man called Towler or Troller. It was he who gave his name to the gill because it was here that he was confronted by the barguest.

This infamous apparition was locally known as a spectre-hound because it sometimes assumed the rough shape of a dog.

Barguests feature in many Yorkshire folk stories and I have recounted some in my *Folk Tales from the North York Moors* as well as others which appear in this volume (see Grassington and Arncliffe). Although each barguest differed slightly from story to story, there were certain basic characteristics. A barguest was a fearsome apparition which was said to herald death; it often manifested itself shortly before the death of a local person. One method of avoiding death was to keep water between yourself and the barguest.

A barguest could have many differing shapes, but it was usually that of an outsize domestic animal such as a donkey, goat, dog, pig, calf, cat or even rabbit, although any other animal might be featured. A barguest could never be mistaken for a normal domestic animal because it had huge bright, saucer-like staring eyes and feet that left no marks on the ground. Its awesome appearance was accompanied by a fearsome roaring sound which is variously described as howling or shrieking.

The name probably comes from the German 'berg-geist' which means mountain demon; or it could be a bahrgeist which is the spirit of the bier. In the north of England, the spelling varies between bargest, bierguest, barguest, bahrgeist and boguest.

There were other similar mythical beasts which had specialised haunts – kirkgrims appeared near churches while padfoots terrified night-time travellers, often in towns.

Troller's story ended in tragedy but before I relate it, there is a tale of one man who met a barguest and survived. He was one of the cobblers of Thorpe (see 'Thorpe') and was returning from Fountains Abbey to

Thorpe. He arrived at Troller's Gill as night fell and found himself having to negotiate this terrifying place in the darkness. Hardly had he taken to the path between the high cliffs when he heard the sound of hoofs and saw some ghostly horsemen pass him by.

These were members of the infamous Ghostly Hunt, spectres in search of the soul of human babies who had died without being baptised. Some called these spectres the Gabriel Ratchets or Gabriel's Hounds – in fact, it was probably a skein of wild geese flying overhead with their eerie calls. But it was sufficient to terrify that nervous cobbler, and, in spite of his fear, he entered Troller's Gill.

It was then that the feared barguest made its appearance. He said it was as big as a small bear, yellow coloured and with great staring eyes like saucers. There was a shaggy sort of a smell about it as it approached him, and he thought the moment of his death had arrived. But he had unwittingly safeguarded himself because the stream of water lay between him and the barguest; he kept that stream between himself and the creature and so survived to tell his tale.

But such luck was not on the side of the man who gave his name to the chasm. I have no firm date for Troller's awful confrontation with the barguest, but the story relates his stupid decision to attempt to defy the creature. Having decided on this reckless adventure, he rose secretly from his bed at midnight and made his way towards the chasm. Either just as he started his journey, or perhaps a little way towards the chasm, he came upon some secret night-time festivities being enjoyed by 'an elfin band', but this did not deter him. He continued towards the gill with only the dim light of night to guide him.

As he approached it, the roar of the waters sounded like a voice from a haunted tomb, so some old verses tell us, but the foolhardy Troller decided to continue. He was determined to face the terror and would not be deviated from his self-imposed task. In the chasm, he sat down for a rest beneath an old yew tree and with an ash twig drew a magic circle on the ground as a form of protection; then he turned around three times and kissed the ground three times, believing that these age-old rituals would keep him safe. Then he actually called out in a loud voice, daring the Spectre Hound to confront him. He must have been horrified at what happened next because something like a whirlwind materialised; the sky grew stormy, the torrent of water grew more turbulent and very noisy, and a kind of lurid flame or spectral light illuminated the terrified man.

And from out of a cleft in the rugged cliffs there leapt the awful creature with its characteristic shrieking and terrible wild barking. Its huge saucer-like eyes were aglow and some reports say it dragged a clanking chain as it savaged the man who had dared to challenge it.

Next morning at dawn, a shepherd was making his way through the gill when he found Troller's body lying beneath the yew tree, his face frozen in horror. The old account says,

> 'And marks were imprest on the dead man's breast,
> But they seemed not by mortal hand.'

Troller was buried in Burnsall churchyard and his grave was later covered by a crop of pretty blue harebells.

2   Arncliffe –

Bertha and the Barguest

There are several stories of barguests in the Yorkshire Dales and an account of their general demeanour is given in the chapter on Appletreewick.

One tale features a barguest at the delightful village of Arncliffe in Littondale. I drove into Arncliffe from Settle, crossing the mighty hills via Kirkby Malham and Malham Tarn. It was an astonishing drive, sometimes along a narrow road between high dry stone walls, sometimes through gated stretches and some across lofty open reaches with twists and winds, dips and climbs. In parts, it was breathtaking; there was the loneliness of the community at Darnbrook, the sheer grandeur of the scenery and some of England's most incredible views.

Arncliffe, whose name may mean 'cliff of the eagles' (arn coming from erne, meaning eagle), is one of the prettiest and most charming of the high Dales villages. It is one of four, plus one hamlet, located along the short but pretty and sparkling River Skirfare. The hamlet is Foxup, high in the hills on the northern side of Penyghent, while the other villages are Halton Gill (one of the highest villages in England), Litton which gives its name to this remote dale, and Hawkswick which is a further reminder of eagles and the birds of prey which hunted among these distant fells.

Another theory, however, is that the prefix 'arn' referred to a farmstead or dwelling in Anglo-Saxon times, and that the village's name therefore means 'dwelling or farmstead beneath the cliff'. And there is a cliff, known as

Blue Scar which overshadows the village. Another old name for the village was Amerdale, a name used by Wordsworth in his epic poem about the White Doe of Rylstone (see Rylstone), and that ancient title is commemorated in the popular Yorkshire TV serial 'Emmerdale'. In the first months of that programme, the village which featured on our TV screens as Beckindale was in fact Arncliffe, but due to its great distance from the studios in Leeds, the programme had to make use of another Dales village whose name Yorkshire TV must not divulge.

Arncliffe and its dale also appear in another guise, this time as Vendale in *The Water Babies* written by Charles Kingsley. He was a guest at Bridge End House and his visits to Arncliffe as well as nearby Malham Cove inspired him to write his classic book. In the book, the house became Dame School, and Tom first encountered the Water Babies under the bridge between this house and Arncliffe's church.

Arncliffe's history goes deep into our ancient past; the caves on the surrounding hills gave shelter to primitive people with Dowkabottom Cave being a home for Celts while hunting, for Iron Age people, for various people during the Roman settlement of the Dales, and even for robbers hiding from their victims.

Its entrance is over 1,000 feet above sea level and during the last century, three human skeletons were found in the cave along with personal adornments and weapons; Roman coins, including a denarius from the time of Trajan were found, as well as the bones of many animals, long extinct. It seems the cave might, at one time, have been the home of wolves, this area being frequented by them until the fourteenth century.

The most curious discovery, around 1860, was a bazalt adze of a type later discovered in New Zealand. Relics of primitive settlements dating to the time of Christ have been discovered upon the fells with rough tracks leading from one Dales community to another. The Vikings settled here too, the deserted settlement of Cosh reminding us that a shepherds' hut in the Scandinavian mountains is called a *kosh*.

In more modern times, Arncliffe has seen a little of the industrial revolution because in 1793, a cotton mill was established here, but the building has been converted into flats. The tiny church of St Oswald dates back centuries too, even though the present structure dates chiefly to the last century, having been 'restored' first in 1796 and again in 1841. It contains a parchment list of men from Arncliffe who fought at the battle of Flodden Field in 1513 beside which is a pike probably used in that fight.

The first church was probably a wooden structure built in Saxon times, and later the Normans erected a stone building, the present chancel resting upon those Norman foundations.

In its remote setting, and surrounded by hills which bear reminders of life dating back thousands of years such as the Giant's Graves, it is not surprising that Arncliffe, and indeed the whole of Littondale, has its share of folk stories.

One involved a Littondale wisewoman called Kilnsey Nan whose real name was Nancy Winter. She was alive in 1820 and lived in a corner of the Manor House at Kilnsey. This was once owned by the monks of Rievaulx Abbey who used it as a farm and grain store, but Nan was considered a fortune teller of some renown. She used a crystal ball for her work and always carried a live guinea-pig in her bosom. She told fortunes by using a pack of cards and a divining rod. She travelled widely, even as far as Skipton where she told fortunes and sold charms. She even opened a shop in Skipton to make commercial use of her talents.

But the most famous and, if the stories are correct, the most skilled was Bertha who lived in a remote cottage near Arncliffe. She became known far and wide as The Wise Woman of Littondale. Few records of her skills remain, but one account appears in an old volume called Hone's Table Book. The writer gives a first person account of his meeting with Bertha and this is what occurred. He knew of Bertha's reputation and was determined to meet her, so he located her cottage which stood in a lonely gill near Arncliffe. It was a wretched hovel and his visit was towards the end of summer or even in early autumn some time in the early years of the eighteenth century.

When he knocked on her gate, a woman's voice invited

him inside and he found an old woman sitting on a three-legged stool beside a turf fire. She was surrounded by three black cats and a sheepdog and asked what he wanted. He explained that he had long wanted to meet her and to observe her perform some of her incantations.

She said she believed that he doubted her powers, that he regarded her as an imposter and that her skills were little more than trickery, but nonetheless invited him to be seated at the side of her humble fire for half an hour.

'In less than half an hour,' she told him, 'you shall see such an instance of my power as I have never hitherto allowed any mortal to witness.'

He entered the house, noting on the walls some pictures of famous sightseers like Nostradamus, Merlin and Michael Scot, the thirteenth-century astrologer and court physician. He observed a cauldron, a sack whose whole contents he never learned, three stools, an old table and a few pans.

Once settled beside the low fire, he waited. After a few minutes, she announced she was about to begin her incantations, but ordered him not to interrupt. Then she drew a chalk circle on the floor and in the centre placed a chafing-dish filled with burning embers. On this, she placed the cauldron which was half full of water. She asked him to position himself at the side of the circle away from her, which he did, and she then opened the sack.

Inside was an assortment of objects which she threw into the cauldron; she called it her 'charmed pot' and he noticed things like bones of different sizes, the dried carcases of small animals and a skeleton head. While throwing in these ingredients, she muttered in a strange language and he did hear the word 'konig', this being a Norse word for king. (As a matter of interest, the name of the nearby village of Conistone is derived from Cuningestone, meaning 'hillside of the kings'.)

Eventually, the water boiled and Bertha offered our witness a glass full and asked him to view the cauldron through it. He did so and was amazed to see the figure of a person enveloped in steam and as he stared at the shape, he realised that it was a close friend of his. He was dressed in his usual clothes, but looked pale and unwell. This made him tremble with fear, and then Bertha put out the fire and removed the cauldron. She now asked if he doubted her powers, demanding that he state whether or not he regarded her as an impostor, but he hurried to the door, wishing to leave.

She halted him, saying, 'Stay, I have not done with you.'

She then offered to show him something even more wonderful than the apparition of his friend. To witness this, she explained, he must go to Arncliffe Bridge at midnight tomorrow, and look down into the water on his left. She assured him that he would not be harmed nor was there any reason to be afraid. He demanded to know more, but she refused to elaborate, and when he asked if he might take a companion, she refused.

If he was not alone, the charm would be broken. He must do as she asked, nothing less, nothing more. He promised he would do as she instructed. He went to Arncliffe Bridge in daylight, but saw nothing unusual, but during that day could not concentrate upon his normal way of life. And then, at midnight, he went to Arncliffe Bridge.

We are told that it was a beautiful night, with a full moon sailing peacefully through a clear, cloudless sky. Its beams danced like streaks of silver lustre upon the clear waters of the River Skirfare while the moonlight gave peculiar shapes and outlines to the surrounding fells. He could make out the shapes of abbeys and churches, towers and spires, Gothic arches and ancient castles and other strange shadowy shapes. All around was total silence, broken only by the murmuring of the stream. It was, he wrote, a scene of perfect calm and beauty.

He waited on the bridge as instructed; quarter of an hour passed, then half an hour and then an hour, all with no occurrences. There was nothing but silence about him; he could see nothing and hear nothing. He was about to leave, thinking he had been tricked by Bertha, when the church clock struck twelve. He had arrived an hour too soon! So he settled for another long wait, gazing into the stream.

Then he heard a low moaning sound and the water was suddenly disturbed without any apparent cause, then it settled down and resumed its calm flow.

He looked but could see nothing and found nothing that

might have made that low, moaning noise. Now frightened by the event, he turned towards his father's house, his father apparently living in Arncliffe, and as he walked he became aware of a huge dog like a Newfoundland, heading towards him. It crossed his path and gazed at him. He thought it was lost and spoke to it.

'Poor fellow,' he said. 'Have you lost your master? Come home with me, I'll make use of you until we find him.'

The huge dog turned to follow him, walking silently at his heels, but when our narrator arrived at his father's house, the dog had vanished. He searched the village, but never found it.

Next morning, he returned to Bertha's lonely shack and found her, as usual, seated close to her fire. She asked him what had happened last night and he said nothing, except for the mild disturbance of the stream. She asked him to think again and after some prompting, he remembered the large dog.

He told her what had happened to it, saying that it probably belonged to a traveller passing through.

'That dog,' she told him, 'never belonged to anyone mortal: no human is his master. The dog you saw was a barguest – perhaps you have heard of it?'

Our story teller adds that he told Bertha he had heard stories of barguests, but did not believe them. He regarded them as legends, but added that if the animal was truly a barguest, then someone would shortly die.

Bertha agreed, saying that a death would occur, but not his. She refused to elaborate and he left her hovel. Three hours later, he learned that his friend, the very man whose image had appeared in the steam above her cauldron, had that morning committed suicide by drowning himself in the river, at the very point below the bridge where he had seen the turbulence in the water.

3   Austwick –

The Austwick Carles

In ancient times, many nations boasted stories of simpletons and foolish behaviour. Examples include the inhabitants of Phrygia in Asia Minor, the Tracians of Abdera, the Greeks of Boeotica, the ancient Jews of Nazareth and the Germans of Swabia. As we say in Yorkshire, the folk who lived in those places were more than a bit daft. They were very daft!

So far as England is concerned, perhaps the most famous daft folk were the inhabitants of Gotham, a village in Lincolnshire, but the truth is they were not at all stupid; they were only pretending. The story arose because the people heard that King John was going to instal a hunting-lodge at Gotham but the villagers did not want it. They knew they would be expected to contribute towards its expenses and many would be required to work there when they had better things to occupy them.

And so each time the King came to Gotham, the local people pretended to be simpletons by doing something idiotic. As the King's men witnessed these peculiar happenings, they advised him that the people of Gotham were far too stupid to be worthy of contact with His Majesty, and so the King and his men passed on. He decided not to instal his hunting-lodge there and so the people of Gotham won their little battle.

As the men of Gotham said, 'More fools pass through Gotham than remain in it.' Thus the men of Gotham became known as the Wise Men of Gotham, even though stories of their foolishness are still told.

They once tried to prevent a cuckoo from flying away in the autumn. They realised that when the cuckoo arrived in spring, it seemed to bring fine weather, but when it departed in the autumn, the weather became worse. They decided that if they could keep the cuckoo all the year, they would be sure of enjoying warmer, sunnier times and decided to imprison the bird. When it appeared in a tree, therefore, the menfolk of Gotham all stood around it, holding hands to make a human cage – but the bird flew away over their heads. Cuckoo Hill is a reminder of that event.

On one occasion, King John's men found them trying to drown an eel in a pond; others were seen rolling cheeses down a hill and when asked what they were doing, said the cheeses were bad and so they were sending them back to Nottingham. Others once dragged some empty carts and waggons up a hill, saying they were going to use them to shelter a wood from the sun's rays. These are just a few examples of their simple logic.

One of the earliest collections of their pranks was called *Merie Tales of the Mad Men of Gotam, gathered together by A.B. – Phisike Doctour*. This was published in the sixteenth century and tales of stupidity by the Wise Men of Gotham continue to entertain us.

England boasts other simpletons such as the Borrowdale Follies, the Bolliton Jackdaws, the Chiseldon Follies and the Yabberton Yawnies, and in most cases, very similar stories are related about them. Several have tried to wall in the cuckoo, for example. As one might expect, Yorkshire has its own 'Gothams'. There are the Calves of Walton (see Walton) while among the others are some taunts of Yorkshire places, many being used by one town or village to tease or annoy another. Many appear in short verses – here are some examples:

Hutton Rudby –	Hutton Rudby and Enterpen, Far more rogues than honest men.
	* * *
Great Kelk –	Great Kelk where God never dwelt

And honest man never rode through it.

* * *

Romaldkirk –   Rum old church, rum old steeple,
Rum old parish, rum old people.

* * *

Raskelf –   A wooden church, a wooden steeple,
Rascally place, rascally people.

* * *

Osset –   where they blacklead the tram lines

* * *

Nafferton –   where they shoe ducks by the stream.

* * *

Marsden –   where they put pigs on the wall to listen to the band.

* * *

Great Ayton –   where they walk through the river to avoid wearing out the bridge.

* * *

Cotherstone –   where they christen calves and kneeband spiders.

* * *

Slaithwaite –   where they tried to take the moon out of the beck.

* * *

Stillington –   If you wish to find a fool,
And do it without mistake,
Take the first you meet in Stillington
In Easingwold or Crayke.

* * *

Stokesley –   Stokesley's learned all it knows from Great Ayton fools.

* * *

Well and Snape –   Where they grin and gawp
And bray hard water soft
With a clothes prop.

*   *   *

Plain of York –	Where they use a scythe for a knife And a rake for a fork.

These are just a few examples of Yorkshire daftness and criticism and perhaps the most famous simpletons in the Dales are the legendary Austwick Carles, carles being an old word for simpletons.

Austwick is a lovely village set in a hollow among the Pennine fells close to the shelter of Ingleborough mountain. It dates to the time of the Norse invaders and its name means 'east settlement'. Some four miles from Settle, it stands quietly off the A65 between Skipton and Clapham, the latter village being known as the home of the Yorkshire magazine, *The Dalesman*.

Austwick's Church of the Epiphany is fairly modern but some of the houses are much older – there is an Elizabethan house and several cottages dating back two centuries or more. Interesting examples overlook the tiny village greens, one of which bears the restored market cross while the hall, a small, fortified manor house, dates to 1573. One bygone industry was weaving and this continued until around 1850, in a building which can still be seen.

A pleasant walk to the north of the village via Town Head and Crummack Lane reveals the curious Norber Boulders, massive rocks that were carried here by ancient glaciers. They were abandoned on their present site some 1200 feet above sea level where centuries of erosion through rain, wind and weather have removed the limestone beneath. Thus they stand on tiny platforms or pedestals looking very much out of place.

Officially known as glacial erratics, they stand on Norber Hill which is of pale limestone, but these dark greenish-grey rocks are composed of Silurian slate and grit. In the world of geology, they are unique and very famous, even if they can be described as freaks of nature.

They have endured the erosion whereas their hilltop resting place has not, and so they stand like weird sentinels above the village. Some of the smaller rocks are scattered haphazardly around the area which forms the entrance to the minor valley known as Crummackdale. These peculiar rocks draw visitors to Austwick while the hills around are riddled with caves bearing odd names like the Boggart Roaring Hole, Lost John's Cave, Rumbling Hole, Death's Head Hole and others.

But in the world of folk stories, Austwick's name lives on in the antics of the famous carles. Perhaps these stories, or variations of them, can be found in other places where simpletons lived. One example is the attempt to wall in the cuckoo; for a long time, Austwick was known as Cuckoo Town even if the story is also claimed by Gotham.

The Austwick Carles, however, went one better by erecting a wire fence to keep out the fog and there are many other tales.

One concerns an Austwick man who fell into a deep pool. His companions watched him sink but made no effort to rescue him, even when he failed to surface.

As they stood and watched, bubbles began to rise from below and when they broke, it seemed they were saying, 'The b...b...b...best's...at t'b...b...b...b...bottom....'

Upon hearing this, they all jumped in to find out what he had discovered on the bottom!

A famous Austwick story concerns the lost whittle. This was the only knife in the village and so it was shared by all. It was very sharp and was used for the manufacture of sticks and other implements made from wood. Whenever it was not in use, it was kept in the branches of a tree on the village green and it was an unwritten rule that whoever used it must always return it to this place.

One day, the carles had some peat cutting work to undertake on the moors above Austwick. It would take all day and this meant taking a picnic meal. Someone gave them a large piece of cooked meat and so they decided to take the whittle with them, to cut and share the meat. But when they had carved their meat, they realised there was no tree in the vicinity and so a problem arose – where could they place the whittle so that it would not be lost?

They debated this problem for some time until one of them, wiser than all the others, noticed a shadow of a cloud. The shadow was on the ground, the only such shadow on that deserted moor, and so he said, 'I know, we'll place it on the edge of this shadow, then we shall know where to find it.'

And so they did.

They continued their work for another two or three hours, but when they had finished, there was not a cloud in the sky. There was no shadow either. They searched every possible place for that shadow, but never found it – and so they lost their whittle. It has never been found.

Another story concerns a farmer of Austwick who needed to remove a bull from one of his fields. He said it would need nine men to lift it over the gate …

One carle was concerned about wood pigeons eating his corn but when he tried to shoot them, they always saw him coming and flew to safety. So he bent the barrel of his gun so that he could hide behind a tree and shoot around corners – but he shot himself in the back.

Another one was asked to take a wheelbarrow into another village and he decided he would take a short cut across the fields instead of going by the accepted route along the lanes. On the way, there were some twenty-five stiles – and so he had to lift the heavy wheelbarrow over every one of those stiles.

In another case, a farmer noticed that his thatched barn had become overgrown with grass. It was sprouting between the layers of straw and he wondered how to get rid of it. Then he realised that cows ate grass and decided that if he lifted a cow on to the roof, it would clear away all the growth. The story does not say whether he succeeded.

On another occasion, the carles had walked over to Settle market and afterwards had enjoyed drinks at a local hostelry.

They walked back at night; it was pitch dark and as they strolled along the lanes, quite merry with the ale they had consumed, one of them found himself lagging behind the others. Then he heard a little voice calling 'Tak him, tak him, tak him.'

He thought he was being followed by a mischievous sprite and asked his companions to wait for him … he ran to them and told them his story, and they all listened. Sure enough, they heard the same repetitive voice. 'Tak him, tak him, tak him.' They could not see the sprite or elf, but decided that they should attack him before he took their friend. They armed themselves with sticks and began to beat the earth in the lane, hoping to either frighten off or kill the evil sprite.

But every time they stopped, they heard the little voice, still calling 'Tak him, tak him, tak him ...'

In desperation, they decided to flee from the creature which by now had assumed the supposed proportions of something like a barguest, or at the very least, a robber or even someone who was going to kidnap them all. And so they ran all the way home ...

But when they arrived, the little voice was still calling 'Tak him, tak him, tak him ...'

But in the light of the window of a cottage, they realised what it was. It was a watch which the slower of them had bought in Settle market; it was in his pocket, going, 'Tick tock, tick tock, tick tock.'

One tale concerns the worries of the carles about the safety of their village because a cliff towered behind it and its face was covered with large boulders. They threatened to roll down and destroy everything in their path. They worried about this for many months, arranging meetings to discuss the problem until the wisest among them produced a brilliant idea.

'I have noticed a sturdy oak tree,' he said. 'Why don't we tie a rope around it, and around all the boulders, and so the tree will hold them back.'

'Where is the tree?' asked one.

'On the top of the cliff,' he said. 'Right on the edge.'

And so they roped the tree to all the boulders below it ...

The stories are not restricted to male carles, however, for there is one tale of an Austwick woman who was returning home one moonlit night. She had been visiting a neighbour and as she walked by the stream, she saw a large cheese floating just under the surface. She tried to take it out with her walking stick, but failed and ran to ask her neighbour to help. She came with her own stick, and then some men arrived with garden rakes and all tried to drag the cheese to the side. But no one could do so.

It was a reflection of the moon in the water.

On another occasion, the carles of Austwick formed a brass band and were soon entertaining neighbouring villages with their music.

So successful was the band that their conductor entered them for a major competition in Bradford and off they went to the city to play. And, surprisingly, they won first prize.

The journey back to Austwick, and the resultant celebrations, made them late and so the conductor told them not to wake the villagers as they returned to their cottages. And so they walked down the main street in their stockinged feet – while playing *See the Conquering Hero comes!*

4 Barden Tower –

The Shepherd Lord

Barden Tower looks like the ruin of a castle rather than the relic of a mere tower, but it stands above the Wharfe on the site of a former hunting-lodge used by the powerful Clifford family of Skipton Castle. The present structure is not the original, however. The first fell into disrepair and the present building is a replacement, also repaired. This imposing stone-built bulk in its splendid setting beside the River Wharfe echoes with memories of some stirring and historic events and it has played its part in perpetuating one of the most enduring folk stories of this region.

Barden is not a village but comprises a scattering of farms and houses along the B6160 between Bolton Abbey and Burnsall. The narrow, stone-built Barden Bridge, which crosses the Wharfe near the Tower, is said to be one of the prettiest in the Yorkshire Dales, while the countryside surrounding this delightful part of Britain is some of the nation's finest. The famous strid is but a short walk away (see Bolton Priory) and the long-distance Dales Way footpath follows the banks of the river between Bolton Priory and Burnsall. Evidence of the Tower's continuing attraction can be judged by the fact that car parks exist near the bridge and the Tower, while part of the Tower (the former priest's house and chapel) has been made into a restaurant.

Among the fells and gills of Barden Moor to the west is Lower Barden Reservoir which is noted for its bird life with Upper Barden Reservoir beyond. A footpath runs across these hills to the south of the reservoirs, linking

Rylstone with the minor road from Skipton to Barden before continuing to Bolton Abbey. It is interesting to speculate whether this path was used in ancient times by Emily Norton and her pet white doe as they walked together from Rylstone to attend Mass at Bolton Priory (see Rylstone).

If Emily did walk that way, she might have seen the distinctive bulk of the first Barden Tower in the distant valley, for construction began in the eleventh century. It was then a fortress from which the surrounding forest was administered, a forest then being an area of parkland full of deer and other beasts of the chase, rather than a large wooded tract. Indeed, the name of 'Barden' comes from *barden* meaning wild boar, for this landscape was territory for the boar before it became extinct.

In 1310, the Tower passed into the hands of the powerful and famous Clifford family who were to be associated with Skipton Castle for many successive generations. It seems the Tower was then little more than a small, insignificant building, almost a ruin, and it was used chiefly as a shelter by gamekeepers – it was one of six similar towers within the Forest of Barden and for many years, it seems to have served no other purpose.

Then the famous Shepherd Lord decided to make it into his home. He extended and renovated the old building until it was fit to become his own private, secluded and rather modest dwelling house. He built the chapel and favoured these premises instead of the ancestral splendour of Skipton Castle.

So who was the Shepherd Lord and why has he become part of the folklore of the Dales? Is his life story true, or is it merely a legend based on some rather slender facts?

The legend of the Shepherd Lord begins with the Battle of Towton near Tadcaster. Tadcaster lies within North Yorkshire between York and Leeds. This terrible conflict, during the Wars of the Roses, took place on Palm Sunday, 1461 and some 36,776 men died in a battle which raged for more than ten hours in a blinding snowstorm. It is said to be the bloodiest battle ever fought on British soil and legends tell us that the waters of Cock Beck which flows past the site ran red with blood for three whole days afterwards. When its waters later entered the Wharfe, they were still stained with red, the red colour remaining in the Wharfe until it joined the Ouse further downstream.

The Yorkists were wearing their emblem of white roses and the Lancastrians wore their red ones during that battle, and it is said that the wild white roses which grow at Towton are still flecked with red because they grow from the blood-soaked earth.

One man who died in that battle was the ninth Lord Clifford of Skipton Castle, a supporter of the Lancastrian cause, but it was some time before news of his death reached his widow, Lady Clifford. Eventually, a messenger arrived with the news that Lord Clifford had died in battle, aged only twenty-six. Shakespeare was not kind to this Lord Clifford, dubbing him Black Clifford or even The Butcher. He was given this nickname because of his cruelty to others; it was claimed he had decapitated the Duke of York and carried the head to the Queen on a pike. But whatever his reputation, his death left a young widow with three children at Skipton Castle. There were two boys and a girl.

Lady Clifford knew it would not be long before the revengeful Yorkists came to dispose of her estates and to murder her husband's young heirs. She decided to hide her children from the vengeance of the Yorkist Edward IV and his supporters, and there is no doubt her foresight saved their lives. Her estates were taken over by the King's followers, but by then Lady Clifford's children were already safely hidden. But not for long.

She had fled to her father's large country estate at Londesborough near Market Weighton in the East Riding of Yorkshire, taking the children via Otley, Tadcaster and York through a complex network of deserted country lanes.

But her hunters knew of her father's estates and decided to search them – fortunately, Lady Clifford heard of their plans in advance. She was able to flee in time, sending the youngest child, Elizabeth, to live with a member of the domestic household as the maid's own child; she sent her second son, Richard, overseas to Flanders and knew she must find somewhere extra safe for her eldest son, Henry. He was now seven years old and was the rightful heir to the Clifford estates, so he, above all, must be safeguarded.

Lady Clifford had a wide circle of friends and acquaintances, but it was to a faithful member of the staff of one of her distant contacts that she turned. The man was a shepherd and his wife was a homely, trustworthy woman who had no children of her own. The couple worked on the fells around Threlkeld near Keswick, on land near the first Threlkeld Hall which was then owned by Sir Lancelot Threlkeld. Sir Lancelot, it seems, loved Lady Clifford and indeed they were married after the death of Lord Clifford at the Battle of Towton, but in the interim period, young Henry Clifford learned to work as a shepherd on the lakeland fells.

He lived a rough life, far removed from his true role as Lord of Skipton Castle. His foster parents had no money and indeed, if he had shown any wealth in his dress or demeanour, local suspicion would have been aroused. Although he was accompanied by his faithful old nurse, he often went barefoot and spent most of his time dressed in ragged clothes.

He slept in an outbuilding on a bed of straw and ate the simple meals of his protectors. This was their way of life and it became his. The boy and his nurse adapted well, the trusty old nurse eventually dying to leave the boy alone in this new world. Sir Lancelot wisely kept his distance and before long, the small boy forgot all about his earlier life.

As he matured into a sensible, wise young man, he grew to love the outdoor life and the work of a shepherd; he became knowledgeable about wild creatures and life in the open air but he never learned to read or write. His tastes were simple and unrefined, his friends were the children of the people of the fells and his pastimes were their pastimes. None knew of his true identity and he remained in Threlkeld throughout his maturing years. He was there from the age of seven until he was around thirty or thirty-one, a total of some twenty-four years. I do not know whether he realised that Lady Clifford, now Lady Threlkeld, was his mother, but it is evident that she did keep an eye on his life and progress. She never lost faith in her belief that, one day, her son Henry would assume his rightful role.

That opportunity came in 1485 with the Battle of Bosworth, the last of the battles of the Wars of the Roses. Richard III was defeated by Henry of Richmond who became Henry VII and with this win, the fortunes of the Cliffords were restored. Having attained the age of thirty, Henry was now acquainted with his true role.

All the former exiles were allowed to return and many cast off the disguises they had assumed over many years. And among them was Henry, Lord Clifford.

It is said that when he took his seat in the House of Lords, the members were surprised to see a poorly dressed man in his early thirties who looked like a farm labourer. He did not walk upright as a man of quality might, but instead trudged down the aisles in the manner of a country yokel. He was grimy, his hands were thick and his fingers tough from manual labours, and he admitted he could neither read nor write. He had come to claim his inheritance and spoke with the thick dialect of the Cumberland fells with a total lack of refined behaviour. He was utterly out of place – and yet this was Lord Henry Clifford, the rightful heir to vast estates in the Yorkshire Dales and the Lake District.

His case was proven and so he assumed his rightful inheritance of Skipton Castle and its splendid estates in the Yorkshire Dales and further afield. But the new Lord Clifford was unhappy among the family splendour; he did not like the refinements of his expected way of life and instead of entertaining the nobility of the area and being host to their upper-class ways, he sought solace in the open air and spent hours walking the fells and exploring the Dales. Opulence, grandeur, wealth, pomp and ceremonial were of little interest to Henry, the tenth Lord Clifford.

It was during one of his explorations on the Barden forest portion of his lands that he came upon the ruined hunting-lodge. A quick examination of its structure and condition convinced him that this should be his future home, not Skipton Castle.

He refurbished the old lodge, extended it and incorporated other buildings such as the chapel, a farm house and some cottages, then made it his home. He lived there for most of his life, only visiting Skipton Castle whenever his presence was unavoidable. He married and produced a son who, much to the sorrow of his father, turned into a wild, womanising young man who became an outlaw for a time and who ransacked several religious houses for the sheer fun of it. That he was an embarrassment and nuisance in and around Barden and Bolton Abbey was never in doubt, and this youth eventually became the first Earl of Cumberland and he was a friend of Prince Henry, later Henry VIII. The Cliffords had many links with the royal family and royal blood ran in their veins, but the gentle tenth Lord, while concerned about the behaviour of his son, was content to remain quietly in Barden Tower.

He learned to read and write; he was found to be of very high intelligence and soon made friends with the monks at Bolton Priory. He walked there every day to attend Mass, later joining them in learning about astronomy and chemistry. He studied the heavens and the plants of the earth, and became a very learned and clever man.

His learning was soon equal to that of the knowledgeable monks; they had taught him well. This Lord Clifford, unlike his father and indeed his own son, or those who had gone before him, was no fighter and warlord; he liked peace and tranquillity. He was loved and respected as a gentle person by all who knew him, including his many tenants.

In 1513, however, he found himself drawn into a new battle, this time the renowned Battle of Flodden Field fought on a hill in Northumberland. He had, by this time, reached sixty years of age and it was evident that he had inherited all the battle skills and military genius of his forebears. He led an army of men from the Craven district of the Yorkshire Dales and reports said that he displayed all the warlike qualities of his ancestors and he helped the English defeat James IV of Scotland in that decisive battle. Then he returned to his sanctuary at Barden for a further ten years, continuing his research into chemistry and astronomy with the aid of his friends, the monks of Bolton.

He died on 23rd April, 1523, aged about seventy, and is thought to have been buried in the choir of his beloved Bolton Priory. He died known as 'The Good Lord Clifford'. From time to time, his son came to Barden Tower to live, if only for short periods, using only the hall and the kitchen. From later accounts, it seems that future owners made use of the tower only for the occasional refreshment and rest while hunting.

The Shepherd Lord's son did not enjoy the solitude that his father had loved and gradually, the old house fell into disrepair. Of all the Lords of Skipton, only the Shepherd Lord thought it was fit to live in permanently, his love of the primitive way of life never leaving him. His successors allowed it to fall into disuse from around 1589.

It was around a century later that the redoubtable Lady Ann Clifford decided to restore the tower. Several of the family houses had fallen into disrepair in those troubled times and so she restored Barden Tower, making it into the building that we can see today. She carried out the restoration between 1658 and 1659, marking the occasion with a carved stone plaque above a doorway. That can still be seen. The tower remained in good condition for a further two centuries or so. For a time between 1670 and 1680 it became the home of the Earl of Burlington's family (said to be the rightful owners while Lady Ann was busy with the restoration, thinking it belonged to her family!) and its last occupancy was probably around 1774. That tenant was thought to be Juliana, the countess dowager of Burlington.

After that date, it was robbed of the lead from its roof and some of its ancient timbers and roofing. It was never repaired. Some cottages, thatched with heather, remained in its grounds until 1872 but they have now disappeared and for a time, the Shepherd Lord's chapel was used as a place of worship by the public.

One of the last rooms to remain in use opened from the chapel, and until 1860 it was known as The Lord's Room. Thus the influence of the Shepherd Lord continued until that time and, it could be argued, it still remains in Barden Tower.

Tourists now admire the old Tower and take

refreshments within its grounds, thus continuing the tradition of generations of Cliffords who used it for rest and refreshment during their hunting expeditions.

5   Bedale –

Molly Cass and Other Witches

Tales of witches were circulating in and around Bedale even at the turn of this century, with folk memory keeping alive some of the more durable yarns. These were not witches who rode on broomsticks and danced naked in woodland glades, but were generally old ladies who were reputed to bewitch cattle so that they failed to produce milk or who might put a curse on a crop to prevent it ripening. They just might attempt to forecast the future if requested.

Bedale was not particularly noted as a centre of such ladies, although one or two stories have survived. Instead, it was, and still is, a quiet market town in the foothills of the Yorkshire Dales. It stands on the edge of the huge Vale of Mowbray between the Rivers Swale and Ure and in some respects, is the gateway to Wensleydale. The A684, which climbs the length of Wensleydale, passes through Bedale on its route from Northallerton via the A1 at Leeming Bar. Bedale is placed sufficiently far from the A1 to avoid the continuing rumble of its passing traffic, and yet, in bygone times, it was close enough to be an important centre for stage coaches. In the time of Daniel Defoe, it was famous for horses. It had, and still has, a busy market on Tuesdays which attracts villagers from the surrounding dales.

Its coaching links attracted highwaymen. Many inn-keepers in this vicinity were in league with the so-called Gentlemen of the Road and indeed in 1812, the licensee of the Kings Head at nearby Kirklington became a highwayman. The long straight stretch of the A1, once known as The Great North Road, which passes to the east of Bedale is a former Roman road which became known as Leeming Lane. It was along this isolated road that the highwaymen lurked as they awaited the wealthy passengers on the slow-moving coaches. Some of them used the grisly Hand of Glory during their raids – see my *Murders and Mysteries from the North York Moors* for stories of this ghastly charm.

Today, Bedale is an interesting mixture of old and new buildings, many of which line the long main street with its wide cobbled borders and slender market cross. At the top of the main street is the massive and splendid church of St Gregory which has a fortified tower. It once boasted a portcullis, a reminder of its role in repelling raids by the maurauding Scots. The tower provides one of the finest examples of a fortified tower anywhere in the north of England. Parts of the tower date to 1330, with the top storey being of the fifteenth century, while the nave stands on the site of an early Saxon church, and part of an Anglian cross stands inside. The north aisle is some six hundred years old while a pair of alabaster figures of a knight and his wife are said to be the finest medieval sculptures in the country.

It is that of Sir Brian FitzAlan (b.1245/6), Lord of Bedale and a viceroy of Scotland, the last of his family line, and his wife, Muriel, lies at his side. There is more of interest in this beautiful church, including its crypt. Outside, just within the gate to the churchyard, is a tiny stone building, now a gift shop; the date 1674 is above the door, for this was once Bedale's grammar school.

Bedale has no claims to be a tourist centre like some of the prettier market towns of the Dales, yet it did once achieve fame as a rope-manufacturing centre as well as being the home of the famous Bedale Hunt.

There are some fine buildings here with the main street boasting several fascinating shops which occupy ancient accommodation. The Kings Head, for example, has some excellent carved panelling but another old building, the Old Moot Hall, which stood to the west of the market cross, has disappeared and so has Bedale Castle built by the FitzAlans. Its inns are welcoming and the old town does possess a quiet charm which many find relaxing and endearing.

Among the surviving witchcraft tales is one about Dolly Ayre who lived nearby at Carthorpe. She could bewitch cattle and had to be persuaded to remove whatever curse or spell she had imposed. In one case, she cast a spell upon an entire herd of cows belonging to a man called Tommy; he went to see a wise man called Sammy Banks in an effort to find a way of removing Dolly's spell.

The wiseman listened and then drove a peg of witchwood (mountain ash, also known as the rowan) into a part of the witch's home, then pressed another protective charm through her keyhole. Then, at midnight, the wiseman burnt something which produced an awful smell – the narrator of this tale never knew what produced the smell, nor what had been thrust through the witch's keyhole, but it seems it did produce results.

One cow died, but the remainder recovered and so it was assumed the charms had worked.

The same narrator, an old man called Richard Kirby who lived at Carthorpe, told another story of Dolly Ayre's powers. It seems that a tenant farmer had once done a favour for Dolly, itself a dangerous thing because witches could misinterpret or misunderstand any kindness towards them, however small. In this case, however, it seems that the kindness was accepted by Dolly and she was grateful. The chance to show her gratitude arose when the tenant farmer was one of several who were competing for larger and better premises. Sadly, Dolly's friend lost and another man moved in.

But, if the stories are correct, Dolly used her witchcraft skills because when the new tenant arrived, he found the words BAD LUCK written in blood-red letters on every door and window shutter. Underneath every message were some other hieroglyphics which no one could understand, and those who saw them knew it was the work of the witch, Dolly Ayre.

As the tenant and his wife moved their furniture into the house, they put some pans on to a high shelf, and for no explicable reason, it collapsed and its heavy load fell upon and killed a child of the ingoing family. The villagers also regarded that as an example of the power of Dolly Ayre. The new tenant left the farm very quickly and Dolly's benefactor moved in.

Perhaps the most curious story is that of Molly Cass, a witch known locally as Awd Molly. She lived in a cottage close to Leeming Mill near where Bedale Beck enters the River Swale.

She was feared in the locality and had the gift of seeing into the future, often frightening the local people by announcing their impending deaths. One example is given in the story known as The Nine of Hearts.

Four men were playing cards in the mill buildings. One was called Braithwaite, another was George Winterfield, another was the miller and the fourth is not identified. It was late at night and dark outside as the four settled into their game. Then an odd thing happened.

Eight times in succession, George Winterfield was dealt a hand which contained the nine of hearts. This caused some excitement among the players, and then one of them wagered a guinea against Winterfield's shilling that it would not occur a ninth time. Winterfield accepted the challenge and the cards were dealt. But before Winterfield could pick up his hand to examine the cards, Awd Molly poked her head around the door.

'Put thy brass in thy pocket,' she said. 'Thy brass is not for him and his is not for thee!'

Her reputation was such that both men removed their money from the table, neither wishing to incur her wrath, and then she came into the room and examined the cards, still lying face down on the table.

She looked at George Winterfield and said, 'George, thoo's got it again. Take up thy hand and see.'

Nervously, he examined his hand of cards and saw she was right – for the ninth time in a row, he had been dealt the nine of hearts. She went on,

'George, thoo's gotten it hard enough. Thoo's had it eight times already, and the Old 'Un's in thee now. He'll not leave thee till he's gotten thee altogether! Thoo's thrown away thy chance, so I've pitched it into the Swale – the Swale's waiting for thee, George, it's going to be thy bridal bed. Go now, the longer thoo waits, the longer thoo'll stay.'

George knew that her words indicated something terrible had happened to his fiancee, the girl he had promised to marry but whom he had kept waiting for far too long. He had not treated the girl well; he had been cruel and hurtful towards her, and so the awful words from the old witch clearly terrified him. He answered,

'I'll wed her! Give me another chance. I've rued all I've done.'

'I'm not often in the mind to give one chance, let alone two,' Molly replied. 'Go thy way. Thy bride's waiting for thee in a bed of bulrushes. Oh, what a bridal bed!'

George Winterfield fled from the mill, promising that he would go immediately to his fiancee and marry her. She had been so faithful to him, so trusting and honest as she had waited all these years.

As he left, Molly called after him, 'Goodnight, George. All roads lead to the Swale tonight.'

No one is quite sure what happened next. Some say George lost his way in the darkness, others say the witch's words caused him to lose his reason, but the next morning the bodies of George Winterfield and his fiancee were found lying on a bed of bulrushes in the deep waters of the River Swale. They were side by side, tangled in the rushes and sedges, and deep under the surface. Friends hauled them out, but both were dead.

It was learned that the girl had drowned herself before George arrived on the scene, so after his fright by the witch, he had never seen her alive; it seems he then joined her in her watery grave.

In the years that followed, it was said that people brave enough to walk beside the Swale at midnight, close to the point where the bodies were found, would see the corpse of a girl float past, swiftly followed by that of a man. They would eventually move closer together as they floated into the bulrushes – and then they would disappear.

6   Bolton Priory –

The Boy of Egremont

Bolton Priory stands close to the A59 Harrogate to Skipton Road and is but a short walk from the village known as Bolton Abbey. Sometimes, these slight differences in name lead to confusion, especially as there is another place called Castle Bolton not far away in Wensleydale (see Castle Bolton). In this case, it is the Priory which is associated with one of the region's more enduring folk stories, that tale known as The Boy of Egremont.

The Priory was established in the twelfth century in a magnificent open setting beside the River Wharfe as it curves gently through the fields and wooded slopes of this beautiful part of Wharfedale. There is a famous view of the Priory from Bolton Abbey through the noted 'Hole in the Wall' – and the viewpoint is precisely that. A hole in a wall. Through a band of trees, this view also embraces Bolton Hall which stands close to the priory. Originally, the Hall was the Priory gateway but it was sold after the Dissolution of the Monasteries by Henry VIII and turned into a hunting-lodge. It became the home of the Dukes of Devonshire who own the surrounding property and among the paintings in the house is one of a youth in hunting-costume. He is accompanied by two dogs and it is thought to depict the Boy of Egremont.

Today, Bolton Priory, in its splendid setting near the Wharfe, is a major tourist attraction. Like so many religious foundations, much of it was demolished by Henry VIII in the course of his Reformation, but in this case the nave remains intact and is now in use as the Anglican parish church of St Mary and St Cuthbert.

There is a long and fascinating history to the Priory but its predecessor did not occupy this site. In 1120, a priory was founded for Augustian Canons at Embsay which is some two miles north of Skipton and about four miles from Bolton Priory. The benefactors were William de Meschines and his wife, Cecilia de Romille. They dedicated that first priory to Our Lady and St Cuthbert, a priory being governed by a prior rather than an abbot. An abbot governs an abbey; a prior is of lesser rank.

Cecilia de Romille was the heiress of Robert de Romille who owned huge estates in what is now called the Craven district of the Dales and she was a devout Catholic. She donated many of her lands to the priory at Embsay, including the manor and lands of Embsay, the church of Holy Trinity at Skipton and the chapel at nearby Carlton. In time, further lands were given to the priory, and these included an estate at Stratton, plus the village and mill at Kildwick. The conveyance of the Stratton estates was done in an odd manner – they were ceremoniously handed over by laying a knife on the high altar of the church and this was witnessed by the monks and by Cecilia and her son-in-law.

He was William FitzDuncan who was the nephew of David, the King of Scotland.

It seems that this community flourished under the protection of Cecilia; eventually, she had two sons and a daughter called Alice or Adeliza, known variously as Adeliza de Romilly or Adeliza des Meschines. In many stories, she is known as Lady Alice, which is what I shall call her. When Alice's parents and two brothers died, she assumed their 'de Romille' surname and inherited their vast estates. In addition to their lands in Yorkshire, they also owned estates in Cumberland, at Egremont in particular.

Egremont lies about five miles south of Whitehaven on the Cumbrian coast; it boasts a delightful market place and ruined castle. The ancient castle had walls twenty feet high and a tower rising to more than eighty feet. On its site above the river it was in an imposing and defensive position, guardian of the family lands and home.

According to legend, Alice became the proud mother of two fine sons but was soon widowed. Shortly afterwards, one of her sons also died. He was the eldest and so the younger boy became heir to massive estates in Cumberland and the Yorkshire Dales. There is little doubt that Alice worshipped her son and taught him all the things he ought to know about the administration of the huge tracts of land he was to inherit. She took him with her to view the lands, livestock and buildings and the people came to know him and like him.

Because he was born in Egremont Castle, he became known as The Boy of Egremont. It was the fate of this child that has led to the creation of a long-surviving legend which explains why the monks of Embsay uprooted themselves after more than thirty-three years, and transferred their priory to a new site at Bolton.

Historians disagree with the legend. The snag with legends and folk stories is that they change almost with every new telling and in time, it is difficult to distinguish truth from fiction. William Wordsworth wrote the story of The Boy of Egremont in an epic poem called 'The Force of Prayer' and the story has received attention from many other poets and writers. The problem with Wordsworth's tale is determining whether or not it is based entirely upon the legend or whether he has incorporated some known facts or his own brand of fiction.

Accordingly, I will give an account of the legend and let the reader consider whether it has any factual links with the foundation of Bolton Priory.

The legend tells how the Boy of Egremont came to stay at Bolton with his mother. The boy was probably called William, but his precise age is not given. He decided to go hunting in the woods which surround Bolton as they stretch along the banks of the Wharfe and had with him his faithful greyhound. Boy and dog were inseparable companions and went everywhere together. As they explored the woods and river banks, they came to a place where the river narrows to such a point that it seems possible for a young man or woman to leap across.

On each side there are large boulders, some of which have blocked the route of the Wharfe to force it through a narrow chasm before continuing its flow downstream. It roars through that slender gap with tremendous power to form a boiling cascade. Like so many other adventurous youths, the Boy of Egremont tried to leap across. He made the fatal mistake of holding on to the leash of his greyhound and although he encouraged the dog to leap with him, it held back at the last moment, nervous of the noise of rushing water. The boy lost his balance and fell backwards into the raging torrent where he was carried away by the swift-flowing current. He and his dog were drowned.

That part of the river is within easy walking distance of Bolton Priory and is known as The Strid. Visitors are warned not to attempt to leap across.

As Wordsworth wrote:

This striding place is called the Strid
A name it took of yore;
A thousand years hath it borne that name,
And shall a thousand more.

Even now, it is said that countless people have lost their lives while trying to leap across the deceptively narrow chasm with its seething rush of white water, and today the river continues to flow between the slippery, dangerous rocks.

It is said that a falconer at work in the woods witnessed the accident to the Boy of Egremont and did his best to revive the drowned youth, but he failed. He then had the terrible task of informing Lady Alice of the tragedy. It is said that he went to her, bearing a look of profound grief, and did his best to break the news gently.

He asked, 'What is good for a bootless bene?' These curious words were his way of asking 'What follows when all hope has gone?'

From the expression on his face, Lady Alice sensed he brought news of a tragedy and replied, 'Endless sorrow.'

She had loved her son so much that she decided to erect a very special monument to his memory and wanted to build it as close as possible to the scene of his death. Beside the River Wharfe at that point was a large, flat open field on a rounded promontory and so she gave it to the

Augustinian Canons of Embsay. They were already in receipt of much support from her wealthy family, and it took very little persuasion for them to move from the rather exposed site at Embsay to a more gentle and sheltered location at Bolton. They moved there around 1154 and immediately began building.

The new priory flourished. Landowning families in the area lavished money and gifts upon the monks. The register of benefactors included nationally known names like the Percys and the Cliffords, and the priory owned churches at Harewood, Keighley, Skipton, Carlton, Kildwick, Marton and Broughton.

By the end of the thirteenth century its annual income was £867 17s. 6d. (£867 85p), a huge sum at that time. It owned 2193 sheep, 713 horned cattle, 95 pigs and 91 goats, and the generosity of its patrons enabled the monks to build their fine church. The choir and chancel were completed by 1170. Over the years, more buildings followed, including the cloisters, refectory, dormitory, kitchens and cellars. The prior had his own splendid lodgings with a private chapel and there was a fine guest house for visitors. There is no doubt it was popular with visitors, too popular in fact – one account says it was over-burdened with them and the books do show heavy expenditure on food and drink, especially on feast days.

The gateway followed, with lakes, parkland, fish ponds, trees, gardens and outhouses, and soon the priory was rich with plate, relics and other valuables. It was a flourishing community with many guests, and it was also a busy farming enterprise – on one occasion, one thousand and ten sheepsheerers were hired for one day to cope with the flock. It was not all easy living – the priory ran into debt due to the vagaries of farming, such as a fall in the price of sheep, diseases among their livestock and crop failures. Added to this were raids by outsiders – on several occasions it was razed to the ground by the maurauding Scots, especially between 1316 and 1321. After Bannockburn, the priory was left in ruins, its crops burned, its livestock slaughtered and its valuables removed.

The monks fled to the safety of nearby houses – on one

occasion, the prior fled to Lancashire and his monks hid in Skipton Castle – and then there were floods …

In addition, the monks were criticised for their lavish life-style when people outside were starving and homeless, but in spite of their tribulations, the priory survived – until the Reformation caught up with this flourishing community. On 25th January 1540, Henry VIII's commissioners arrived and the priory was surrendered to them by its last prior, Richard Moon. He was responsible for further building work and in fact had partially constructed the west tower as the commissioners arrived – that tower was never completed. The builders' materials and equipment remained for many years afterwards, the local people long believing that the monks would return to complete their work. They never did.

At the Dissolution, there were fourteen monks in residence and the imposition of the new state religion ended Bolton Priory's life as a Catholic establishment. It suffered further ransacking, but the nave survived the ensuing destruction and is now used as an Anglican parish church.

It is said that the family of Nortons (see Rylstone) are buried somewhere within the Priory, all of them in an upright position, but excavations have not substantiated the story. In 1854 some nineteen coffins were discovered, one of them almost seven feet long, but none has proved to be that of the Nortons.

Even today, there are accounts of ghostly monks being seen in the grounds, some in broad daylight, and a ghostly horse is said to appear at the Strid from time to time; a sight of this spectral mount heralds disaster to anyone who sees it.

The rise and fall of Bolton Priory is a stirring tale, but is there any truth in the legend of the Boy of Egremont?

It is known that Lady Alice did exist; she was also known as Alicia or Adeliza. She did have a son and he was called William, although her deceased father was also called William. This may also have been the name of her husband. In 1315, a pedigree of the family was exhibited in Parliament when it was proved that William was her son – and her only son. Thus the tale of two sons is false.

One theory is that her son William later died in an accident at The Strid, and that the monks took advantage of her grief and wealth (she was by then a widow) to persuade her to finance their move from Embsay to Bolton which was a far superior location. So what came first – the Priory or the death in the Strid?

Whatever the truth, the legend does live on and the account of the Boy of Egremont is one of the enduring folk stories of the Yorkshire Dales.

7   Bradford –

The Tongueless Boar

Bradford, beautifully set in a deep valley off Airedale, has a long tradition of working closely with the sheep farmers of the Yorkshire Dales and it has grown from a modest Dales town into a prosperous and thriving city which is Britain's most successful wool trading centre.

Once, not many years ago, it had the reputation of being a black and smoky industrial town, riddled with back-to-back houses and factory premises, but the modern Bradford has managed to rid itself of that image. It is now bright and cheerful, with its beautiful stonework cleaned and renovated to reveal some fascinating buildings rich with character and history. It is now a centre for visitors to the Dales and offers comfortable accommodation with good restaurants.

It is now one of the country's focal points for students of the woollen industry, with colleges boasting excellent textile departments, and a range of museums depicting the development of colour in textile printing as well as a wealth of industrial and social history. Bradford's National Museum of Photography, Film and Television is unrivalled and boasts the largest screen in the United Kingdom, while there are lots of splendid parks which offer peace and solitude.

Its fifteenth century parish church became a cathedral in 1920 and Bradford's innovative contribution to the social welfare of the nation includes free education for all, school meals for poor children, the introduction of school doctors and a range of pioneering social work in hospitals and clinics. It remains a progressive town which is proud of its history and proud of its situation on the edge of the Yorkshire Dales.

It hardly seems the place to provide an enduring folk legend, but a close look at the city's coat of arms, granted in 1847, will reveal the source of one enduring tale. The shield depicts three horns of the kind blown during ceremonial events, underneath which are the words 'Labor Omnia Vincit', but for the portion of crest at the top of the shield there is the side view of the head of a boar. It is facing to our left and its mouth is open to reveal a pair of useful tusks. The whole head is displayed before the trunk of a tree.

Inspection of that boar's head shows that the animal has no tongue.

The reason for this is given in a curious folk story. It dates to the time when Bradford was a tiny community in the hills, with only a few simple cottages surrounding its church and manor house. On the hills which encircled the village, there was a dense forest which was the haunt of a massive, savage wild boar. It was not afraid of attacking people, especially those who ventured into the woods to hunt, or to gather wild fruit for pies or sticks for their cottage fires.

The animal became a great menace but no one could get near enough to kill it with spears, swords or other means. In desperation, the Lord of the Manor said that he would give his lovely daughter to any man who could slay the boar and it was not long before word of this offer reached all the young men of the district. Many had seen the lovely girl and knew she would be a wonderful wife – besides, she would one day inherit all her father's wealth and estates. The offer was one which no right-minded man could refuse.

Among the suitors was a quiet young man who worked at the manor house. He was a pageboy, with little prospect of wealth or position, and during his work he had grown to know and love his Lord's daughter. She liked him too, but marriage was out of the question due to their widely differing social backgrounds. But he decided to take up the challenge.

Being an intelligent youth, he did not charge into the woods on horseback armed to the teeth like so many others. Invariably, they alerted the boar. Instead, he crept about on foot to learn the movements of the huge beast, silently observing it during the day and also at night, when it slept. Eventually, he discovered that it did have one favourite place where it often slept. The den had several entrances and exits, and so he decided to dig a pit before one of the exits. The plan was that when the beast lay asleep one night, he would rouse it and encourage it to pursue him by that route.

Then it would fall into the pit and he would be able to despatch it. Thus the page boy carefully set his trap.

His plans were a success because the boar did fall asleep in the expected place, and he did arouse it. He shouted and cursed at it, threw stones and generally succeeded in annoying the angry animal until it started to chase him. He ran forward, skirting his deep pit and sure enough, the boar ran across the flimsy surface, falling with roars of frustration into the deep hole. And there, with the aid of a long spear and his sword, the page boy was able to kill the beast.

All that remained was to persuade his Lord that it was he who had rid the neighbourhood of the terror and then he could claim his bride. He decided to cut out the boar's tongue and show that to his master – that should be sufficient proof.

He did so, and set off back to the village, still on foot. But a knight from another dale had also been hunting the boar with a view of winning the hand of the fair lady, and when he heard the commotion, he had concealed himself behind some trees to observe the pageboy in action. He saw him kill the animal, but the knight decided he would claim to have done so. Thus *he* would win the hand of the desired girl.

He leapt into the pit and cut off the boar's head, mounted his horse and galloped back to Bradford with his trophy. His superior speed upon the horse meant that he reached the mansion ahead of the pageboy. Wasting no

time, he sought the Lord to announce his news and held
the boar's head high.

The Lord listened in admiration and was about to hand
over the girl, when the pageboy arrived. Quickly, he
realised the situation and shouted that it was he who had
slaughtered the beast. The knight scorned the boy's story,
indicating the head which now lay on the floor before the
Lord and his daughter.

'I have slaughtered the beast, and this is my proof!' he
beamed at the Lord and his daughter.

But the pageboy pointed to the mouth of the severed
head and asked his Lord to examine it.

'Sire,' he said, 'there is no tongue in the mouth of that
beast – when I slaughtered it, I left the head behind, but
cut out the tongue. I have it here.'

He then produced the tongue from the pouch on his
belt. The Lord knew the pageboy was telling the truth. The
head without its tongue proved nothing, but the tongue
and the tongueless head together were proof of his
prowess.

The pageboy and the Lord's daughter were therefore
married and lived happily ever after, and the story is
commemorated in Bradford's splendid coat of arms.

8   Brimham Rocks –

Lovers' Leap

One of North Yorkshire's most popular places for weekend visitors is the sixty-acre complex of huge, weirdly shaped boulders known as Brimham Rocks. They are surrounded by a patch of moorland some 387 acres in extent which is known as Brimham Rocks Country Park. At an elevation of almost 1,000 feet above sea level, the Rocks present some strange and fantastic shapes which have led to countless stories and theories about their origins. They command staggering views across the countryside, especially down Nidderdale. There are views to the distant North York Moors too, and it is claimed that, from some positions, it is even possible to see York Minster's towers, twenty-five miles away. As a bonus, there is a wealth of animals and birds to be seen, ranging from red deer and hares, to birds of prey and Dalesbred sheep.

Brimham Rocks are located about one mile south of the B6265 Ripon to Pateley Bridge road, the junction of the lane leading to the rocks being at Crossgates. From the opposite direction, they can be approached from the village of Summer Bridge which lies on the B6165 between Pateley Bridge and Ripley. Today, the Rocks are in the care of the National Trust which operates an information centre and shop on the site. There are spacious car parks too.

The shop/information centre is currently open from April until October, although the Rocks can be visited at any time, quite free of charge. In so doing, visitors are asked to keep their dogs on leads due to the proximity of grazing livestock.

Folklore suggests this collection of strangely shaped rocks is the work of the devil or some other mysterious agency while others once thought they were the result of volcanic eruptions. Another tale was that the druids were somehow responsible and that the rocks were used during their ceremonies. Scientists, on the other hand, tell us that Brimham Rocks are Britain's finest example of the effects of wind erosion, being the result of centuries of wear and tear by the wind, rain, frost and the other vagaries of British weather in this remote region. In their lofty position, the softer portions of the rocks have been carved away by the unremitting action of the wind and weather, leaving the tougher portions of stone to present these grotesque and fascinating shapes. They do look as if they have been sculptured by some giant hand, but their appearance is due solely to nature's art.

They are an integral and curious part of the moorland scene, with heather, bracken, bilberry and other growths competing for attention, but their fame began in the seventeenth century when the first visitors trekked up the slopes to view them at close quarters. One later visitor was a Major Hayman Rooke who was the first to discover that some of the huge boulders would actually rock on their bases.

Four of them are now known as Rocking Stones, the largest weighing several hundred tonnes, and from this has grown a legend that the rocking stones can only be moved by an honest person. It is a joke in Yorkshire that no Yorkshireman has ever achieved this!

In order to appreciate the names of the other rocks, they need to be viewed from the right angle and right distance, and this can sometimes take a long time to establish, unless one is given advice by a guide. As an aid to self-help, there are maps in the car parks which identify the better-known rocks. Among them, therefore, are the following:

The Dancing Bear, the Idol Rock, the Yoke of Oxen, the Pivot Rock, the Chimney Rock, the Druid's Skull, the Needle's Eye, the Cannon Rock, the Druid's Telescope, the Lamb, the Druid's Reading Desk, the Pulpit, the Baboon's Head, the Oyster Shell, the Elephant, the Tortoise, the Flower Pot, the Sphinx, the Rhinoceros, the Druid's Profile, the Frog, the Dog, the Rabbit, the Tiger, the Boar's Snout, the Hippopotamus, the Druids' Altar, the Druid's Cave, the Wishing Stone, the Kissing Chair and others. It is said that somewhere among the rocks is a cave where a witch lived; this is the Abode of the Great Sybil who was said to be even more remarkable at fortune telling than the famous Mother Shipton of nearby Knaresborough.

One old writer said the rocks were like gigantic chess men, some of which appeared to have been turned on a huge lathe while another called them 'nature's ruins'.

But the romantic or artistic person will recognise them from their names, most of which come from the fancied outline and position of the rock in question, with the Dancing Bear claimed to be the most lifelike.

The huge Idol Stone stands on a tiny base only some two feet in diameter, while the Cannon is perforated with holes, one of which is some thirty feet long but only a foot or so in diameter, like the barrel of a cannon. The Wishing Stone contains a hole into which one is supposed to place one's middle finger of the right hand and make a wish. If you can squeeze into the Druid's Cave, it has openings which are like windows looking over staggering views of the Dale. The best time to see these rocks, and to let the imagination conjure images and shapes from them, is during the evening as the sun is setting, casting long shadows across the landscape. It is little wonder that our forebears regarded them as something magical and awesome. Today's children love to explore them and to create their own legends from the sights around them.

But among these rocks are those which contain more than a hint of magic and mystery. A group are linked together by a small natural arch and are variously called the Lovers' Rocks, the Lovers' Stones or the Lovers' Leap. It was from here that a romantic folk story was born.

Years ago, a young man called Edwin lived in a nearby village and he fell in love with a beautiful girl called Julia. Sadly, the girl's father did not approve of Edwin.

9 Burnsall –

The Great Maypole Theft

Burnsall, with its old set of stocks, is a pretty village (pop. 125) which is typical of those among the finest of Dales scenery. Situated beneath the fells in the lush tree-lined valley of the River Wharfe, it has a long street which follows the line of the river and its houses are constructed from the warm brown stone of the region. Some, with their mullioned windows, date to the seventeenth century while the parish church can trace its origins to a wooden building in Anglo-Saxon times. As a centre of early Christianity, Burnsall was called Brineshale by the Anglo-Saxons.

In AD 690, St Wilfred is said to have preached from a rock in the river; that rock is still known as St Wilfred's Pulpit, but another four hundred and fifty years was to pass before the first stone church was built. This was constructed between 1140 and 1150 by Alice de Romille, but there are some hogback tombs and Norse stone crosses dating from the ninth and tenth centuries. The church also contains a glorious medieval Italian carving of the Adoration of the Magi dated 1350 and a Saxon font, while the churchyard contains a sundial and an interesting lychgate with an ancient mechanism. The gate revolves on a central post and a heavy rock, concealed within a wall, ensures its closure. Restored in 1987, it is the only one of its type in Yorkshire.

The church, which is probably the oldest site of Christian worship in the Dales, is noted for having two peculiar vicars, both called the Reverend John Adcott.

There are many tales of their eccentricity. One of them forgot to bring the notes of his sermon so said he would read a passage from the Bible which was worth ten of his sermons. On another occasion, a mischievous parishioner mixed up the pages of his sermon and fastened them together in a totally confused order.

Undaunted, Adcott said he would read it as it was, and said the congregation would have to sort out what he was really trying to say. When a bride refused to take the vow of obedience to her husband, he said he agreed with her and omitted that part of the service. One of the John Adcotts was tutor to the Knaresborough murderer, Eugene Aram (see my *Murders and Mysteries from the Yorkshire Dales*).

In the early years of the seventeenth century, Sir William Craven (see Appletreewick) was a major benefactor to the church and the village, repairing the church in 1612, building the original bridge and providing a grammar school in 1602 which is now the local primary school. This splendid Elizabethan building is next to the church and the upper storey was divided by planks of oak to create boarding accommodation – those features are still there. Girls were admitted in 1860, but it became an elementary school in 1876.

In addition to Sir William Craven, the village has another brush with history.

A farmer's daughter from this quiet village became the wife of a clergyman in Lincolnshire. He was called Nelson and they had a son called Horatio who became one of England's most famous and respected heroes.

Long before the Christian era, Burnsall was probably a thriving centre for pagan worship and ceremonial. There were some ancient holy wells here – Thor's Well is said to be over a thousand years old, and others were dedicated to Saints Margaret and Helen. One of the popular Sunday evening enjoyments for the villagers until the middle years of the last century was to collect the water from these wells and drink it, mixed with sugar.

Another relic of the past is Burnsall's famous maypole which is erected on the village green. For as long as people can remember, this has been a popular focus for May Day celebrations, but on one occasion in 1804 it attracted some unwelcome attention. Among the crowd of Dalesfolk who had come to enjoy the dancing and feasting were some of the cobblers from nearby Thorpe-sub-Montem (see Thorpe). When the celebrations were over, the men of Thorpe began to wish their village had such a fine maypole, for that tiny community could never host such a splendid display of dancing and fun. And as the men of Thorpe made their way home that night, they decided that their village *would* have a maypole. And where could they find a finer example than the one at Burnsall?

Flushed with a sense of adventure, and perhaps merry with more than a little drop of strong ale, they decided to steal the Burnsall maypole and erect it in Thorpe. Several nights later, therefore, the little band of maypole bandits crept into Burnsall and managed to carry off their trophy without rousing any of the residents. When the Burnsall folk awoke next morning, they were horrified to note its disappearance.

They made an immediate search of the surrounding villages and although Thorpe is located very close to Burnsall, its isolated situation caused it to be overlooked, at least during the first session of hunting. But in time, the searchers did climb the surrounding hills and spotted the remote cottages of Thorpe – and when they ventured into the quiet place, there was their own maypole standing proud in that village.

Thus an army of volunteers was recruited from Burnsall and they set out to recover their pole. From the records, it seems that the invaders from Burnsall far outnumbered the men of Thorpe, most of whom were cobblers, and so the maypole was recovered. It was re-erected in its rightful place at Burnsall and although Thorpe residents are welcome to admire it or to join in any of the events around it, that historic incident is still remembered.

Today, there is another sporting event in Burnsall – it is the annual Burnsall Sports held every August on the Saturday following the first Sunday after 12th August.

Locally this is celebrated in honour of St Wilfred although his feast day is two months later, i.e. 12th October. Here in Burnsall, however, ancient inter-village rivalry can be expressed in a friendly manner, and a feature of the sports is the famous and tough Classic Fell Race which is a true test of a Yorkshireman's stamina. The runners climb Burnsall Fell, rising to more than 1,000 feet.

This is the oldest fell race in Yorkshire.

In 1991, history repeated itself. At a cost of £350, the people of Burnsall had repaired their maypole following some storm damage and it lay on the green, newly painted, awaiting erection for Mayday. But on the night of Sunday 28 April 1991 it vanished. By the Monday morning, a lovely new maypole had mysteriously appeared in Thorpe-sub-Montem, cemented into its new base; the pole was remarkably similar to the one which disappeared from Burnsall. There had been reports of overnight activity in Thorpe, including some mixing of cement, but no one there would admit anything ...

10 Castle Bolton –

The Lady who Walked

Castle Bolton should not be associated with Bolton Priory or Bolton Abbey (see page 45). They are several miles apart but rather like those Boltons, these cause a little confusion because the lovely stone village, with its delightful church of St Oswald, is known as Castle Bolton, whereas the giant castle which towers above it is called Bolton Castle.

Castle Bolton can be viewed at a great distance from the A684 as it runs along the Dale. Its solid bulk occupies a very prominent position on the northern slopes of Wensleydale not far from Redmire. It is between Askrigg and Leyburn among a network of narrow lanes well away from the main A684 highway. The castle, still in private hands, does welcome visitors and at the time of writing is open daily from March until November.

Castle Bolton was the stronghold of the famous Scropes whose part in the administration, government and history of England is incomparable. From the Scropes, who came to Bolton in 1284, there have been two earls, twenty barons, two bishops, four High Treasurers, two Chief Justices, a Lord Chancellor and an Archbishop. Many have been honoured as Knights of the Garter, and the family still occupies a prominent position in the public life of Britain, Yorkshire and Wensleydale.

Throughout history, and particularly when the Catholic faith was under attack during the penal times, the Scropes remained faithful to their religion and most of the family still follow that ancient faith. Conversely, they also earned the friendship and trust of many sovereigns, some of them being Protestants. Among the first to gain that trust was Richard Scrope, adviser to Richard II, Treasurer of the Exchequer and Keeper of the Royal Seal. It was he who asked the king's permission to extend his rather ordinary home on the estate at Bolton and the king gave permission in spite of objections from the powerful Nevilles who lived at Middleham, a short distance down the dale. Thus, in 1379, the building of the present castle began and it took a further eighteen years before it was completed. From that time, the Scropes were at the forefront of English history, gaining a mention by Shakespeare and entering the fabric of English administration.

It was Lord Scrope of Masham who conspired against Henry V before setting out for Agincourt, recalled in these words of Henry V from Shakespeare:

'What shall I say to thee, Lord Scroop?
Thou cruel, ingrateful, savage and inhuman creature!
Thou that didst bear the key of all my counsels,
That knew'st the very bottom of my soul,
That almost might'st have coined me into gold,
Would'st have practised on me for thy use?
I will weep for thee,
For this revolt of thine methinks is like
Another fall of man.'

Perhaps because the Scropes were such noted men of history, even Elizabeth I trusted them in spite of their Catholic religion. Her persecution of Catholics is notorious and she was worried in case those of the nobility who clung to their old religion would depose her in favour of Mary Queen of Scots. In particular, the Duke of Norfolk caused her concern because he wanted to marry Mary and restore the Catholic faith, as well as rebuilding the abbeys and priories that Henry VIII had destroyed. Nonetheless, when Elizabeth decreed that Mary Queen of Scots be held in safe custody (possibly for Mary's own safety), it was the Scropes of Bolton Castle who were entrusted with that task. It is now the only remaining place in England in which Mary was held captive and so there has developed a mixture of history and legend associated with this impressive, and at times forbidding, old castle.

One of its darkest places is the dungeon, thirteen feet by nine feet, and without natural lighting; it is hewn from solid rock below the north side of the castle with an entrance through a hole in the floor above. For years, it contained an iron staple to which prisoners were chained. Another of its features was a system of hooded chimneys far ahead of their time. The hoods were suspended over the central hearth and pipes carried away the unwanted smoke to points between the windows. They were regarded as a marvel of their era.

It was to this lonely, solid and almost impregnable stronghold that Mary Queen of Scots was brought in the middle of July, 1568. She had fled from Scotland, crossing the Solway Firth and landing at Workington in Cumberland from where she went to Carlisle. Elizabeth I sent her a message of comfort and ordered Lord Scrope to meet her; this he did on 20th May, 1568 and Mary then chose to settle in England instead of France. She spent time in the houses of the Catholic gentry around the Borders, but Elizabeth could not allow her to become a threat to her English throne. Thus she ordered Mary into safe custody and selected the Scropes, and their castle at Bolton, as the custodians. Mary came from Carlisle via Appleby, crossing the Westmorland border near Kirby Stephen and then coming over the Mallerstang Moors to Hawes, then thence to Castle Bolton by travelling down Wensleydale, then called Yoredale. Accompanying her was her retinue of six personal attendants, twenty carriage horses, twenty-three saddle horses and forty men to look after the horses and other matters. Half of these men were boarded out in the tiny village, at farms and cottages, and the quiet place must have been shocked and surprised by the sudden influx of people and animals. Those not accommodated in the village had to be found space within the castle, and it seems that Lady Scrope had not expected such a large influx of guests. She had to rush out and borrow furniture and bedding from Sir George Bowes, for the Queen was not to be incarcerated within the notorious dungeon.

Instead, she was to be allowed her own apartment with servants and all the attentions befitting a royal guest. Mary was at Castle Bolton for about six months, from July 1568 until January 1569 when she was taken to Tutbury in Staffordshire. Her room at Bolton was in the south-west tower and it had two windows, one of which overlooked the courtyard while the other looked to the west. There is little doubt she was bored and frustrated during her time here – although she was not chained and was allowed out of doors, she was virtually a prisoner with little to occupy her.

It is said that she inscribed her name *Marie R* with a diamond ring on the glass of one of the windows of her room and it was there for many years, even surviving the weather when the castle fell into disrepair. But when someone tried to remove it and take it to Bolton Hall, it was accidentally broken, although the pieces were kept. The castle has had a stirring history – it was under siege during the Civil War when Colonel Scrope was starved into surrender, and in 1647 the York Committee ordered the destruction of the castle. But it remains solid and seemingly indestructible, if a little battered, and is a powerful reminder of the durability of ancient families and their homes.

It has, of course, produced its own legends and folk stories, the two chief ones concerning Mary Queen of Scots. During her incarceration at Castle Bolton she was allowed out of the building, under constant escort and supervision.

At times she was a guest at some local halls and great houses. She enjoyed hunting expeditions too, and upon one of her outings she was a guest for two nights at Nappa Hall which was near Askrigg, some five miles up the Dale from Castle Bolton. The site of the hall remains, although Nappa is now a farm; it was never given the status of a castle although it was the seat of Sir Christopher Metcalfe, one of the famous Wensleydale family of that name. The bed in which the Queen slept remained at the hall for many years and it was there until the middle of the last century, having been preserved. I have no note of its present whereabouts.

One story is told by a woman who, in 1878, was herself a guest at Nappa Hall. She was a small girl at the time and was playing hide-and-seek with the resident farmer's daughter, a girl about four years old. The only lighting in the huge hall came from a log fire and a candle and as the two girls played, someone came into the hall from the lower end. The narrator of the story thought it was the farmer's wife (i.e. her friend's mother) and ran after her, reaching out to touch her dress. It was of Tudor style in black velvet and beautifully cut, and some accounts say she also wore a small hat. But as she reached out, the woman halted and turned around whereupon the story teller noticed her face. It was very soft and beautiful, and after gazing at the child for a few moments, the lady continued her walk.

She disappeared through a door which led up the winding staircase to the angle turret of the west tower. That was where Mary had slept and when the child realised the lady was not her friend's mother, she went to have a look at a portrait of Mary Queen of Scots. She then realised she had seen an apparition of the sad and beautiful Queen.

This is just one of many alleged hauntings by Mary in places at which she slept prior to her execution in 1587. In some cases, she appears anonymously as either the Grey Lady or the Blue Lady, but among the sightings in Yorkshire is one at Turret House, attached to the old manor castle at Sheffield. The ghost of Mary has been sighted there on many occasions. She came here in November 1569 following her departure from Castle Bolton, and stayed for fourteen years, under the charge of the Earl of Shrewsbury. Although the Turret still stands, it is derelict and surrounded by modern housing estates. Another reported Yorkshire venue of Mary's ghost is Temple Newsham House near Leeds where no less a person that Lord Halifax is said to have seen the ghost of Mary one winter night in 1908. A woman with a shawl around her shoulders crossed his bedroom in the firelight and vanished into an adjoining one. The house is said to have been the birthplace of Henry, Lord Darnley, husband of Mary Queen of Scots.

One very durable story of Mary is said to have created the name of Leyburn Shawl, a stretch of hilly fellside a mile or so to the west of that town.

There are some extremely pleasant walks upon The Shawl, with a footpath leading from Leyburn via The Shawl to Preston-under-Scar and thence to Castle Bolton.

Leyburn is a pleasant market town some 700 feet above sea level with five roads leading into it, so making it a busy and important centre for the Dalesfolk. But for those who like to view the expanse of the Dales, a walk upon The Shawl is almost obligatory and access to the path is from the top of the market place, through Shawl Mews to the right of the Bolton Arms Hotel. The Shawl offers stupendous views, sometimes through a band of bushes and trees. Places like the heights of Penhill, the pretty Dales villages and a huge expanse of incomparable scenery are all visible, sometimes with the bonus of hearing the roar of Aysgarth Falls when the River Ure is heavy with flood water. Some accounts say this view is the finest in the North of England.

It was here that Mary Queen of Scots lost her famous bid for freedom when she was at Castle Bolton. Dodging her guards one day, she managed to climb out of a window at the castle from where she fled into the countryside and decided to head for the nearest town. Some reports say she was alone; others say she had the assistance and connivance of young Christopher Norton of Rylston (see Rylston). Maybe he was drawn to her beauty or her royal blood or even her Catholic faith.

But the town to which she fled was Leyburn, and a useful path led from the castle down the dale via the heights above the River Ure. Mary knew the area for she had been hunting here from time to time, always under supervision, but she took that path, running as well as she could and walking when she was tired. But the heavy bushes and briars brushed against her and before she arrived at Leyburn, she heard the noise of pursuit. Horses and dogs were chasing her; a full-scale search had been mounted and she fled in terror now as one of the briars caught her shawl. It was pulled from her shoulders, but she had no time to stop and retrieve it.

As she hurried towards Leyburn, so her guards found the abandoned shawl and knew she had recently passed this way. She was soon caught and returned to Castle Bolton. The place she was caught became known as Queen's Gap, and ever afterwards, that area of fellside along which she fled has become known as Leyburn Shawl. Even now, it is pointed out as the place where Mary Queen of Scots lost her bid for freedom.

Detractors from the tale say that the name *shawl* comes either from 'shaw', meaning wood, or from the old Norse words 'schalle' or 'skali' meaning huts or shelters. Below the Shawl are the remains of some pre-historic dwellings occupied by ancient man.

11 Coverdale –

The Woman in Black

Coverdale's remoteness has preserved it from mass tourism, but it is now being discovered as one of the more delightful minor dales. The River Cover flows from the northerly slopes of Great Whernside and also gathers water from the southern fells of Penhill as it meanders down this peaceful dale. It joins the Ure below Middleham, at East Witton in Wensleydale. A long, winding road passes along the dale between high dry-stone walls to link Middleham in Wensleydale with Kettlewell in Wharfedale and it is surprising to learn that, not so very long ago, this was the route used by stage coaches on their way from London to Richmond. As one drives towards Kettlewell, the immense bulk of the Pennine peaks makes itself known, the dominant ones being Great Whernside and Buckden Pike.

There are several small communities within the dale, including Carlton-in-Coverdale, West Scrafton (where there is a cave called Tom Hunter's Parlour because it once concealed a runaway highwayman); East Scrafton and Caldbergh, with Horsehouse at the Wharfedale end and Coverham at the other. The road wends its way into the hills where it becomes very steep and narrow as it climbs to some 1600 feet above sea level before descending into Wharfedale.

High on the moors beside the road, before the long steep descent into Wharfedale, is a standing stone, bent at a curious angle. It bears a small carved cross on one of its faces close to the top. This is known as Hunter's Stone and is near Hunter's Stone Bank. It was once a route-marker for the monks who travelled between Coverham Abbey and Kettlewell, and according to legend, every time the clock in Hunter's Hall strikes twelve, this stone turns around. Some versions say it performs this trick when the clock strikes one.

Secure on the edge of Wensleydale, Coverham is a somewhat lengthy village comprising splendid cottages and farms built in the local mellow stone, some of which came from the former abbey. This dated to the thirteenth century when it was founded by the Premonstratensian or 'White' Canons. The original abbey was established at Swainby in Swaledale by a lady called Helwyse, daughter of Ranulph de Glanville who was Lord Chief Justice of England in the reign of Henry II.

After a dispute, the abbey was transferred to Coverham by her son in 1214 and occupied a delightful site close to the river. Although it did become a foundation of some importance, it suffered heavily during raids by the Scots and was dissolved during the Reformation. The monks were acclaimed for their 'good syngyng' and were also noted for breeding white horses; centuries later, white horses were numerous in Wensleydale. Oddly enough, the monks of nearby Jervaulx Abbey were also noted for the breeding of fine horses.

Even today, the area remains very strong in the horse-racing world, with some top stables being based nearby at Middleham.

After the Reformation, the buildings of Coverham Abbey fell into disuse and the unwanted stone was used to construct farms and houses. Some slight ruins still remain, but they are on private land although a careful search of the area might reveal remaining widespread evidence of the old abbey.

The church of The Holy Trinity at Coverham was rebuilt in 1854 but is no longer used for worship. This is sad, for it is a handsome building in its isolated site well away from the village. It is here that a curious phenomenon is said to occur. It is said that a person may stand within the churchyard when the church bells are ringing, and yet be unable either to see the church or to hear the bells. The steep slope of the churchyard provides one clue to this, while the noisy actions of a water-wheel, weir and mill drown the sound of the bells. I went to the church to check the legend – and although the bells were not ringing, I could see it was true. The strange old graveyard dips steeply through a gate at one end, with graves in some very odd places, and although the mill is no longer functioning, there is a waterfall which drowns all other sounds – and I could not see the church although I was but a few yards from it.

An old bridge across the River Cover is said to have been constructed by the monks, but Coverdale has few claims to fame.

It was, however, the birthplace of Miles Coverdale, who became the first Protestant Bishop of Exeter and who translated the Bible into English. This was published in 1535, after which he revised it and published a new edition in 1540. He was born in Caldbergh at a hall which was reduced to a farmhouse and he achieved great and everlasting fame through his work in translating the Bible as well as for translating the Apocrypha from German and Latin.

The River Cover also gave its name to Cover Bridge Cheese, made by the monks of Jervaulx Abbey. Upon the dissolution of their monastery, they passed the secret recipe to the Towler family who kept an inn at Cover Bridge. They developed it. It was the soft, plae cheese we now call Wensleydale.

The area, due to its history and associations, is ripe for legends and folk stories, but one has survived the passing of the years whereas many other tales have been forgotten. It concerns the Woman in Black.

Among the delightful walks in the area is one which leads, somewhat indirectly, from a point near Coverham Church via Tupgill and Fern Gill, on to Middleham Low Moor. For many years, the people of Coverham and the nearby communities would never walk that way during the hours of darkness because it was feared they would meet The Woman in Black. The place where she appeared was near a gate at a point known as Courting Wall Corner, a location which was hitherto used as a meeting point for young couples.

Accounts of her appearance were all remarkably similar; it was said that she was a young woman who wore a long black cloak and walked as if in mourning, always shaking her head in deep anguish. There is one story of some people who were visiting the area on holiday; one evening, they went for a drive with a pony and trap and found themselves at Courting Wall Corner after darkness had fallen. As they approached the gate in the wall, they noticed the figure of a young woman waiting nearby and called out for her to be so kind as to open the gate for them. She wore a long black cloak. But when they spoke, she just vanished into thin air.

It was only afterwards that they heard the story of The Woman in Black.

It appears that the tale was based on a love affair that went tragically wrong. A local girl was secretly seeing two men, both of whom were desperately in love with her, and eventually the time arrived for her to make a decision. Which one should she marry?

After a lot of anguish, she made her choice and, to avoid local scandal, decided to elope with him. They would marry elsewhere and start a new life away from Coverdale. But the rival learned of their plans and arranged to meet the girl for one last time. Then he murdered her and buried her body near Courting Wall Corner. The local people were sure that the unfortunate girl's ghost came to revisit the scene of her death.

No one was quite sure of the facts, especially the story could never be proved due to the passage of time, but some years ago, peat-cutters were at work nearby and they discovered the skeleton of a woman, buried not far below the surface. She was never identified, but she was dressed in the remnants of some black cloth.

12   Dalton –

The Giant of Dalton Mill

There are not many stories of giants in the Yorkshire Dales but three are included within this volume (see also Penhill and Sessay). Similarly, there is more than one village by the name of Dalton, with one near Richmond in Swaledale dating to Roman times.

But the Dalton in this tale lies just south of Thirsk, a couple of miles off the A19 Thirsk to York road, and a similar distance from Topcliffe. The main London-Edinburgh railway line runs just to the east of Dalton while the beautiful River Swale flows to the west. Dalton, with its small industrial estate, has few claims to fame but it does have a pretty stream which wends its way beside the village street and a charming, tiny clock tower on the end of the church. Although visited by businessmen, it does not attract many tourists although it does feature in a very old folk story about a hungry and fearsome one-eyed giant.

He terrorised the neighbourhood from his home at Dalton Mill beside the Swale, some distance from the present village, but he did not feast upon bread made from the flour normally produced by such a mill. Instead, he used human bones. He chased and often caught unwary people, especially small children and young women.

After consuming their flesh he saved their bones and ground them to dust with the old machinery of the mill. He then made huge loaves from this gruesome flour and consumed them for his meals.

In an attempt to keep himself in food, he had to travel

far and wide in his search for victims, sometimes travelling as far south as York and Tadcaster or north into County Durham. People living locally knew him and made sure they kept out of his sight; they could hear his heavy tread as he left the mill upon his regular missions on to the moors and into the Dales in his urgent hunt for food. Even those living further afield knew of the hungry giant from Dalton and made sure they always kept out of range of his solitary eye.

But people grew careless and somehow, he usually managed to obtain a supply of fresh victims; in spite of worried parents warning their families about the evil giant, the children forgot or ignored their parents' pleas and played beside the river or in the fields around Topcliffe and Thirsk, many falling victim to the massive giant at the Mill.

But giants were not immortal, even in those times, and they did grow old. This happened to the giant of Dalton Mill and as he grew older and more feeble, he found he could not travel such long distances, nor was he sufficiently agile to capture running children or fit young people. He had to rely on older victims, but they were not so succulent or tasty.

Furthermore, the sheer effort of looking after himself was taking its toll and he decided that he needed the services of a capable assistant. He did have a companion, however; it was a small dog which had strayed into the mill and remained unscathed, but the dog could not help with the lifting and manual work. A willing human was needed.

The giant began to look for a likely fellow. And then, one day as he was searching the vastness of the Vale of Mowbray for victims, his old eye caught sight of a strong youth working in some fields near Pickhill. From a distance, the giant watched and decided that this lad would be ideal.

The boy was fifteen years old and his name was Jack, and the moment he saw the giant striding towards him, he ran for his life, hoping to find shelter in the lush trees that lined the banks of the Swale. But he was not quick enough. With huge strides, the giant overtook him and snatched him from the ground. The giant bore Jack back to the mill, striding through Sinderby, Ainderby Quernhow and Baldersby in his haste to return before night and it was said that, for years afterwards, his massive footprints could be seen in the soft ground beside the river. The terrified Jack thought that he was doomed to die a horrible death, but he was pleasantly surprised when the giant released him inside the old mill, saying that the lad would come to no harm if he would do as the giant asked. Somewhat bewildered by this unexpected turn of events, Jack agreed.

He knew that no other living person had survived capture and reckoned that if he could remain alert and alive, he might be the first to escape the giant's clutches. He was to learn that all the giant wanted was someone to help him in his domestic routine – at times, this was not very pleasant, especially when the giant returned with victims whose bones would be ground into flour, but at least the lad remained alive with a bed for the night and a roof over his head.

Whenever the giant left the premises, he locked the doors and windows to prevent Jack's escape, and whenever he was at home, he always watched the boy most carefully. Even with one eye, the giant's scrutiny never lessened and Jack found little or no opportunity to escape. Even when the giant slept, the slightest noise brought him into instant wakefulness and Jack knew that if he tried to run away through the open door, the giant would catch him within a very few strides. And then he would become part of the giant's next awful meal. So the lad waited. His patience was infinite and he knew that, one day, the giant would be too feeble to detain him. As the months went by, the giant did grow older and more tired and then one year, Jack heard the giant talk about Topcliffe Fair. It had always been Jack's practice to visit the fair, to play the games there, to take part in the contests of strength and skill and to meet the beautiful girls who flocked there. As he lay in his bed that night, Jack decided that he must make a determined and bold effort to attend the fair.

It started tomorrow and lasted for three whole days. In

recent months, the giant had taken to having a nap in the afternoons, especially after a heavy lunch, but as he slept he always kept his knife clutched in his fist. It was the knife he used to cut his terrible loaves of human flour, and so on this fateful day, Jack ensured the giant had a larger and more tasty meal than usual. Sure enough, the giant lay down on his bed of straw and soon fell asleep, his single eye closing against the light of day. Jack knew he must move very quickly and very quietly if he was to escape.

He saw the huge fist relax just a fraction; the handle of the knife moved gently as the giant's grip loosened in sleep and so Jack tried to take it from him. At first, he failed, but soon he had managed to prise the knife from the sleeping giant's hand and at that moment, he awoke. He was awake in a trice, but his age meant that he could not sit up as quickly as he wished and Jack was upon him in an instant; finding the necessary strength, he plunged the knife into that single eye.

But the giant was not killed; he hurtled out of bed, roaring with anger and pain as the blood poured down his face, and he stood before the door to prevent Jack's escape. Then he began to feel his way around the mill, his huge hands sweeping the empty spaces in his search for Jack. He threatened Jack with the mill stones ... he would soon become flour ... the eye would repair itself ... he would hunt again ...

As the huge man roared and rampaged around the mill, Jack spotted his dog. It was picking up the titbits left from the giant's table, something the giant tolerated. It helped to keep the floor clean but now it would help Jack to escape. Jack seized the surprised dog, lifted it high on to his shoulders and crept towards the door. As the blinded giant heard the movement, so his huge hand came down to find out what was causing the noise; the big fingers brushed the dog's back and the dog licked them. The giant accepted that the noise had come from his own dog and returned to his hunt for Jack.

And so Jack went for the door, opened it and ran for his life. He dropped the dog which ran with him, and the pair raced to safety across the fields beside the River Swale. But their flight was unnecessary – Jack's knife had penetrated deeper than the solitary eye. He had pierced the giant's brain and scarcely had Jack fled from the mill when the giant crashed to the floor, stone dead.

Jack's quick thinking had saved the district from further terrible attacks, and it is said that the giant was buried beneath a large mound which is just outside Dalton. It is called Barf Hill but for many years was known as The Giant's Grave. In addition, the old mill once displayed a long piece of iron like a huge blade which was said to be the knife that Jack used to gain his freedom.

Oddly, another giant lived only a mile away at Sessay. Could the two stories involve the same giant? (See Sessay)

13   Fewston –

The Bosky Dyke Boggart, Haverah Park and More!

Fewston boasts a level of drama, mystery and intrigue which far exceeds its modest size. Once known as Fuystone, it was described as 'a wild place with rude people on whose ignorance God have mercy' and it was said the people resorted to the aid of witches to keep the evil eye from harming their cattle, or to help the cows to give more milk. The village and surrounding district are rich with stories of witches and fairies and folk tales, and it has associations with three recent murders which contain puzzling elements. An account of these is given in my *Murders and Mysteries from the Yorkshire Dales.*

Fewston lies in the Washburn Valley which extends north from Wharfedale and it is roughly midway between Skipton and Harrogate in North Yorkshire, just off the A59 road as it sweeps across Blubberhouses Moor. It has a considerable history, with the present church of St Michael and St Lawrence dating to 1697. That date is carved above the door. This is the third church for Fewston and it contains some fifteenth-century remnants; Fewston's first two churches were destroyed by fire which adds another dimension of intrigue to this tiny place. In the fire of 1696, its thatched roof was destroyed and the pitch of that roof is still marked on the tower.

The present church, with its noted stained glass, is of architectural interest because when it was rebuilt in 1697, it was built to the medieval plan with a clearly defined nave and chancel, and not in the style of most other seventeenth-century churches. And when I visited the church, a crime had just been committed – a cashbox, used to contain donations, had been prised out of the wall and forced open.

A visit to the churchyard will also enthral because it contains a gravestone that marks the final resting place of two men, father and son. It records the death of Joseph Ridsdale on 29th February 1823, and his son on 30th February 1802, neither of which dates ever existed. Another tombstone tells a curious story. Joseph Wood, aged fifteen, had driven a cow to Otley for a Mr Holmes, and was late returning home. The worried villagers arranged a search and found him dead, his horse and dog waiting nearby, unharmed. The cause of his death remains unknown. The entire story is inscribed on the tombstone.

Also buried here is Edward Fairfax, a poet and translator, and a member of the famous family of that name. After his death, his former home, New Hall, was flooded and now lies at the bottom of Fewston Reservoir which spreads before the village. It can be viewed through the trees before the church.

Fairfax was noted throughout the country and his work was enjoyed by both James I and Charles I, and yet he believed in the power of witches. He wrote a book on witchcraft and unsuccessfully tried to prosecute some local women as witches.

Nearby Timble Gill Beck was said to be the haunt of witches and also fairies. Children can still be enchanted by a tiny stone fairy bridge which crosses the stream near its entry to the River Washburn. In fact, it is a model which honours a local rambler called Arthur Adamson, but it was here that the Fewston Witches were supposed to meet for their secret ceremonies. These are sometimes known as the Timble Witches, Timble being a nearby hamlet, and they were supposed to meet here, eating around a huge table with the devil seated at one end. The cook was a local woman called Janet Dibb.

There was a ghost here too; it was said to be that of a traveller murdered by poachers many years ago, and for centuries it haunted the area near the fairy bridge.

Another of Fewston's peculiarities is that it was once called the Moving Village. Many of its buildings were cracked and some of their walls leant at alarming angles, so much so that the village became a tourist attraction. The reason was not linked in any way to the supernatural; it was due to subsidence, some of which was blamed upon the construction of Fewston reservoir, now a popular tourist attraction with the adjacent Swinsty Wildlife Reserve. For a village so rich with intrigue and mystery, it is not surprising that it boasts some folk stories. Three tales of Haverah Park follow, but stories of the Timble Gill Beck witches and fairies have dwindled over the years.

I can find no particular tale in which they were involved, other than Fairfax's belief and attempted prosecution at York Assizes.

Fewston did, however, have a boggart. It was known as the Bosky Dyke boggart because it haunted that area of the village. The patch of land in question was sometimes called Busky Dyke, the word busk or bosk meaning bushes or shrubs. They were thick and tall here, and the area was dark and mysterious; the shrubs covered the slopes of a narrow gill through which a small stream and footpath ran. Today, a band of trees still covers the area above the reservoir and a road crosses the earlier haunted part. The people of Fewston were afraid to walk that way at night, and even in the daylight hours, it had some kind of sinister hold over them. But even before the turn of this century, the area was cleared of this scrub vegetation and opened to the light of day, so much so that by 1900 all vestige of its former dark image had vanished.

This was the area haunted by the boggart. A boggart was a ghostly creature which was sometimes confused with a barguest. Barguests are featured elsewhere in this book (see Appletreewick, etc.), and they assumed the appearance of frightening animals whereas a boggart was in human form. Boggarts were sometimes said to be the ghosts of murder victims seeking revenge; one of their tricks was to wait for a rider to pass and then leap upon him and cling to his back and shoulders with clawlike hands.

No amount of effort would dislodge the boggart as it

rode along, at the same time uttering piercing shrieks until the horse and its rider were terrified into galloping to their deaths.

Boggarts, like barguests, were omens of death and were often depicted as having long, straggly hair, wide staring eyes, a cloaked appearance which sometimes concealed a bare skeleton, and a large, heavy chain which they dragged along to make it clank and rattle. Many boggarts were known for their shrieking cries and in some parts of the country, they were known as shrikers or shriekers, and almost without exception, they bear a malicious and cruel streak. A kindly boggart is an unknown thing!

The Bosky Dyke boggart, therefore, would haunt that area of Fewston and, according to old accounts, was frequently seen. He had long hair which hung down over his shoulders, a pair of horrible eyes with which he would transfix his victims, and he dragged the inevitable chain which clanked and rattled as he moved. His own footsteps were noiseless and it seems he favoured areas which were deeply covered with trees and shrubs, and after terrifying his victims, he would vanish down a drain which crossed the nearby road. This was a male boggart, whereas some were female. A female boggart called The Boggart of the Brook used to haunt a bridge at Garstang, across the border in Lancashire. With the clearance of the Bosky Dyke shrubs, the darkness disappeared and ended the hauntings.

In fact, the village school was built on this site in 1878 and the building stands on the very place where the boggart was said to make his appearance. When I called, the houses adjoining the old school were for sale, although there are no known accounts of the school being visited by him! An old poem records the hauntings and some of its verses read:

> Long tales are told from sire to son,
> In many a forest ingle,
> Of rushing sounds and fearful sights,
> In Bosky Dyke's dark dingle.

But lo! there now, as deftly reared,
As if by magic wands,
In superstition's own domain,
A village schoolroom stands.

Where thickest fell the gloom of night,
And terror held its sway,
Now beams the rising sun of light,
And intellectual day.

Before its beams, its warmth, its power,
Let every phantom melt,
And children's gambols now be heard,
Where a fearful boggart dwelt.

Yet softly tread, with rev'rent step
Along the Bosky shade,
There ghosts our fathers feared of old,
Will be for ever laid.

Fewston, for all its charm and beauty, remains a village with a mysterious, intriguing and at times violent past. The murders which have occurred in and around the village since the last reported appearance of the legendary boggart makes one wonder whether its influence is not yet finished.

The stories of Haverah Park are somewhat more cheerful. This is a tract of wild and rocky heather-clad moorland within the Forest of Knaresborough. It extends east from a point a mile or so outside Fewston and stretches towards Beckwithshaw in the hills above Harrogate. On these moors are two reservoirs and the scant remains of John o' Gaunt's castle, which was probably built as a lodge to guard the park when it was rich with deer.

In their ancient and original form, parks were created for animals, especially deer. A park meant an area of forest (which did not necessarily have to contain trees) and it was specifically appropriated for the use of animals of the chase. The name comes from the Latin *parcus* or the French *parque*, and the lawyer, Manwood, defined a park as 'a place of privilege for beasts of venery and other wild beasts of the forest, and of the chase.'

The very first park was at Woodstock in Oxfordshire and was created by Henry I in 1123. To be officially a park, the area had to have a grant from the king, it had to be enclosed with railings, walls or hedges, and it had to contain beasts of the chase, such as deer.

If all the deer were destroyed, it was no longer a park; similarly, if all the fences were removed, it ceased to qualify as a park. A park could not 'lie open'. Once a piece of land qualified as a park, therefore, it was licensed as such and this was done by the king. It was called the King's Grant or prescription, and could only be dissolved by the king under Letters Patent. No man could create a park without this approval and parks were well protected under the forest laws of the time. In some cases, the public could use them and the laws permitted ordinary folk to take timber or graze livestock.

Many of the nation's parks remain, although the rules and uses have changed beyond all recognition – one well-known example is Hyde Park in London which once belonged to the monastery of St Peter in Westminster; it was enclosed to form a park in 1545.

It follows, therefore, that the creation of a park was a very solemn and serious matter which required royal approval, and this means that the manner of creation of Haverah Park is all the more astonishing.

The name may come from *haie* meaning a hedge or fence, and *wra* referring to a species of deer, probably the roe.

Haverah thus means the fenced enclosure for deer – in other words, a park. This reasoning, however, conflicts with the legend of the founding of Haverah Park because, it is said, it is named after a poor man called Havera.

At the time of the story, Haverah Park lay in the midst of the Forest of Knaresborough, a royal forest of some importance, and our story begins during the reign of Edward III (1312-77). The Lord of Knaresborough Forest was the fourth son of Edward, known to history as John of Gaunt. In the final years of his father's reign, John was the effective ruler of England; he was also Duke of Lancaster.

According to legend, therefore, the poor man called Havera was out in the countryside one day, but his journey was difficult because he was an invalid. He had to rely on crutches for his mobility and at that time, it meant he had a rough life. Ordinary activities like riding and hunting were almost impossible for him. But Havera never gave up; he struggled through life and was always cheerful with a deep determination to succeed, especially when others believed he would fail. It was this strong side of his character that won him Haverah Park.

It seems he was hunting in the forest when, by chance, he met John of Gaunt who was staying at his castle. John had with him the usual entourage of officials and friends, but the two men, prince and commoner, fell into conversation. Prince John expressed his concern about the life style of the invalid.

Havera explained how difficult it was to survive, but added that he had no wish to be a burden upon anyone, not even his family. Then he made a brave request.

'My Lord,' he said to John of Gaunt, 'I crave of your bounty. I ask permission for a small quantity of land, just enough for me to cultivate by myself so that I might survive without being a burden to my family and friends.'

John looked at the man; it was evident that he recognised a good man beneath the simple clothes of the rustic fellow and he made this surprising declaration:

'I, John of Gaunt, do give and do grant to thee, Havera, as much of my ground as thou canst hop around in a long summer's day.'

This was, in effect, the necessary grant to make the land into a park, and so Havera accepted the challenge. For his gallant hop around the land, he chose Barnaby Day, June 11, which was then the longest day of the year. This was before the calendar changes of 1752, and Barnaby Day was, by tradition, the date the farmers harvested their hay, being usually dry and sunny.

For Havera, however, there was a different kind of harvest and at the moment the sun rose on that morning, he began his marathon undertaking, struggling around the boundaries of the piece of land upon which he had set his heart. The people came to watch and as the day wore on, so Havera continued his tiring task.

By nightfall, he had almost completed the circuit of a

huge tract of land, and as the sun fell below the western horizon, he was a few feet short. But he was able to throw his crutch across the remaining few yards, to land beside the marker he had placed before starting his trek.

John of Gaunt was true to his word and allowed Havera to keep all that land – it was the land now called Haverah Park.

A second folk story is associated with Haverah Park. A king, whose name is not given, was out hunting one day when he cornered a particularly savage and cunning wild boar. It was in a part of the park which had areas known as High Boarhole and Low Boarhole. The king, who had become detached from his retinue, was about to despatch the boar with his spear when the animal seized it between its powerful jaws and snapped it in two, leaving the king at its mercy. The boar then charged the king, intending to rip him apart with its huge tusks, but a knight happened to witness this and stepped in at the last moment. He used his own boar-spear to halt and kill the animal and saved the king's life. As a sign of his gratitude, that king said to the brave knight, 'You and your descendants may keep Haverah Park for ever.'

That knight was called Ingilby and the family became owners of Haverah Park; they still occupy Ripley Castle some four or five miles away.

Another folk story associated with Haverah Park concerns the young Lord de Lacy whose parents had arranged a marriage for him. He was to marry Lucy, the daughter of Lord Dacre, a man he detested. When de Lacy was riding to meet his intended bride, he noticed a beautiful shepherdess and when he asked where she was heading, she explained she was going to Haverah Mead to tend her sheep. De Lacy said he was on his way to marry Lucy Dacre, but began to express more than a passing interest in the shepherdess, so much so that she told him to leave her alone and go to his intended bride.

As they walked together, de Lacy eventually decided he wanted to marry the shepherdess; he explained how he hated Dacre and how he had never seen his intended bride. He had heard that Dacre was a ruthless man, cruel and dangerous, and not the sort of man he wanted as a father-in-law.

It seems he managed to convince her of his real love and so she mounted his horse while he walked alongside, now a very happy man. He took her to a priest-hermit he knew who lived on Haverah Park, and lost no time in going ahead with his marriage to the shepherdess. He declared that she was his true love; she reciprocated and they rode off to his castle in the dales.

That night, as she lay in his arms, she horrified him by accusing him of being false to his intended bride, and then she said that she was in fact Lucy Dacre. She was the girl he had been sent to marry, the daughter of the hated Lord Dacre, and as an old verse says,

> 'De Lacy gazed, confused, amazed,
> Upon the lovely speaker,
> And the captive now was led to bow,
> Before the great Lord Dacre.'

The legend does not say whether or not the couple lived happily ever after.

14   Giggleswick –
The Nymph of the Well

Giggleswick is famous for its name, its public school and the curious Ebbing and Flowing Well which is to be found about a mile along the road towards Clapham.

Giggleswick has an old village centre, but is now spread along the western banks of the River Ribble in the higher reaches of Ribblesdale, while on the eastern bank stands Settle, a busy and thriving market town with its own attractions. Some aspects of Settle have a decidedly continental atmosphere but the two places are quite distinct and separate communities. The river is a well defined natural boundary even though Settle High School, Middle School and Swimming Baths are all in Giggleswick.

Giggleswick dates to a period long before the Norman Conquest but its precise age is not known. Prehistoric remains of man and beast have been discovered upon the surrounding hills and in several nearby caves. Many artefacts such as pottery, bronze ornaments and glassware are stored in museums both at Giggleswick School and in the Museum of North Craven Life at Settle. Neolithic remnants indicate that people have been living here since the dawn of time. Evidence was found at the tarn – Giggleswick had a natural tarn which was filled in about 1830 and cultivation of the land began three years later.

It was near the site of the present golf course, and during the draining of the water, that an Early Bronze Age canoe was found. It dated to 1600-1400BC and was lodged in Leeds Museum – but it was shattered during an air raid in 1941. Nonetheless, it did indicate the timescale of human occupation of this impressive district.

Today's village centre is a charming collection of old stone houses complete with a market cross, stocks, tithe barn and stream flowing through. One focal point is the fascinating old church of St Alkelda for this probably has ancient links with the nymph of the well. The story of that nymph has almost been forgotten due to the passage of time, but it is included here.

The church dates to the fifteenth century although the interior was 'improved' during Victorian times. The pulpit dates from 1640, an alms box is inscribed 'Remember the pore' and dates from 1684 while the font has a Norman base. The church is dedicated to St Alkelda and it is one of only two churches in Britain to have this saint as patron. The other is at Middleham in Wensleydale.

Alkelda was said to be a Saxon princess who was murdered by two Danish women invaders and although her martyrdom is depicted in one of the stained-glass windows, almost nothing is known about her. The first record of her, so far as Giggleswick is concerned, occurs in the will of James Carr in 1528.

He expressed a wish to be buried 'in the church of Gigleswicke of the Holie and Blessed Virgin Saint Alkelda'. But there are those who say that Alkelda never existed and the following account could be one reason.

In Yorkshire the old name for a well is keld; the Anglo-Saxon was kelda and their word for holy was halig. Thus a holy well was halig kelda or haeligkeld. Variations of this name, such as Hallikeld, still occur in the Yorkshire Dales at Swaledale and Wensleydale, while at Middleham there is also a well dedicated to Alkelda. It is suggested that the name of Alkelda is derived from halig kelda, via Hallikeld to Alkelda.

In the case of Giggleswick, it is claimed that Alkelda used to worship at the village's famous Ebbing and Flowing Well where she also baptised the faithful in its waters. But could Alkelda really be a halig kelda, a holy well? In other words, might Alkelda be an old name for this well and not that of a real person, least of all a saint?

Indeed, when considering the legend, could Alkelda

really be the mythical figure who features as the nymph who was turned into a spring? Is it she who is really featured in the ancient folk story? Primitive people did believe that holy spirits were contained within their wells, many of which were regarded as either holy or magic in some way, chiefly because their waters did not cause illness. We would say this was due largely to their lack of pollution but those people had no such concept.

They believed that the good water was magic or possessed spiritual benefits (see also Threshfield.)

The links between Alkelda and the wells of Giggleswick and Middleham provide scope for discussion and are discussed in my book *Murders and Mysteries of the Yorkshire Dales*.

In referring to James Carr's mention of St Alkelda (above), it is interesting to note that he was involved in the foundation of Giggleswick's famous school. In November, 1507, the Prior and Convent of Durham granted, out of their church land at Giggleswick, half an acre near the churchyard. It was for use by James Carr on condition that he enclosed it and 'at his own proper cost build upon it and keep up one gramer schole' (sic). When Carr died, he founded and endowed with lands, to the annual value of £6 1s. 0d., the Chantry of the Holy Rood in the parish church for the specific purpose of providing a chaplain and headmaster. In 1546, Thomas Husteler was incumbent of the chantry and also headmaster because Henry VIII's commissioners described him as a man 'sufficientlie sene in playnsonge and gramer.'

When the land left by Carr was confiscated under the Chantries Act, Husteler and a man called Malhome made provision for the school to continue, and later Thomas Iveson did likewise and this enabled it to function until it was refounded and endowed by no less a person than King Edward VI (1547-53), the son of Henry VIII and Jane Seymour. His charter was dated 26th May, 1553.

The school has thrived since that time. It has produced many scholars of note and achievement, and the massive copper dome of the chapel, now coloured a shade of green, continues to dominate the locality as a symbol of its durability.

Giggleswick has been host to several famous persons, including George Fox who was placed in its stocks in 1665, and it was also the home of Anne Bankes who married Roger, the cousin of Samuel Pepys. William Paley, the Archdeacon of Carlisle and later Chancellor of that diocese, was author of a noted book on the Evidences of Christianity and he was also a son of Giggleswick – in fact, his father, also called William, was headmaster of the famous school for fifty-five years (1744-1799). And the village achieved a different kind of fame in 1927 when thousands of people arrived to witness the eclipse of the sun.

Towering crags and fells lie to the north of Giggleswick, amongst which are many caves. Some are adjacent to the B6479 road which leads north-west from the village towards Clapham and the Lancashire boundary. This leads to the 300-feet-high Giggleswick Scar and the site of the Ebbing and Flowing Well.

But there are other sights of interest near the well. One is a massive cairn of rocks which stands on the top of the Scar. This is variously known as the Schoolboys' Tower or Schoolboys' Cairn and, if the story is correct, every pupil at Giggleswick School has placed a rock upon it, and so have many thousands of other people who have walked this way.

Another sight is Nevison's Nick or Nevison's Leap. According to legend, the famous highwayman was being pursued from Giggleswick and his horse was tiring. He paused only long enough for it to drink the waters of the famous well. This gave the necessary additional power and strength to evade the would-be captors. It managed to struggle to the summit of Giggleswick Scar and some accounts say it actually leapt to freedom from the top of the cliff!

It is the famous and almost unique Ebbing and Flowing Well which has been of such interest to local people, visitors and experts alike over the centuries. It can be found at the foot of Buckhaw Brow beside the road and it has a stone seat around three sides. A deep trough has been constructed to accommodate its ever-flowing waters but inspection is not easy because there are no parking facilities on this busy road. The well has been flowing since time immemorial – no one can be sure when it made its first appearance, but its remarkable ebbing and flowing capabilities have elevated it into either a magic well, a wishing well, a holy well or merely one of deep scientific interest, the choice depending upon personal whims.

Its water ebbs and flows numerous times a day, rising and falling several inches without apparent reason. Different visitors have reported different timings. Some state that the ebbing and flowing occurs eight times a day, others state six times a day while some confirm that it can happen as frequently as once every six minutes.

When the author William Camden (1551-1623) wrote his famous survey of England called *Britannia*, he said the well was 'the most noted spring in England for ebbing and flowing, sometimes thrice in an hour'. There is little doubt that the frequency does change a good deal, and in dry weather or conditions of drought, there may be very little movement at all. In very wet conditions, the rise and fall can be highly irregular, thus the best circumstances in which to see the rise and fall is during what can be described as normal weather – whatever that is! There are reports of witnesses standing beside the well for hours without noticing any changes. I stayed but a few minutes without seeing any change in the water level.

Various theories have been produced in an attempt to explain this curious phenomenon, but it might be linked to atmospheric pressure coupled with the system of natural syphons which exist deep within the rocks of this area. This part of the fells is particularly rich in underground caves and watercourses.

The mystery of the rising and falling waters, coupled with its sighing sounds, was something our ancestors could never understand and so they regarded the well as mystical and magical. It had all the attributes of a holy well, particularly the ever-present flow of pure water, and so a legend was propounded in an attempt to explain its presence and purpose.

The story goes far beyond the earliest Christian days when in the classical times of Rome and Greece, the gods were pagan, when nymphs lived free in the woodlands and satyrs roamed the countryside. In classical mythology, satyrs were minor gods in human form but with the tail and ears and, in some cases, small horns of animals like goats. Quite often, they were depicted as having the hind quarters of goats and they were noted for being lustful, especially towards the nymphs.

At Giggleswick, an old version of the legend of the well says that a satyr frequented the woods and fells near the village. It seems odd that this word is used in an old English folk story and I wonder whether it was used merely as a poetic convenience, or whether satyrs were said to once haunt our woods. In fact, the creature in the legend is very like another mythical god, Pan. He was also depicted with small horns, animal's ears and the hind quarters of a goat; he dwelt in woodlands and he pursued nymphs.

Like the satyrs, he terrified girls so that they ran off in desperation – from this, the word 'panic' has arisen. Pan was a symbol of fertility and was the god of shepherds and their flocks, but there is one story of him pursuing a nymph called Syrinx because he wanted to make love to her. She fled into the river and he followed; she escaped by changing into a bed of reeds and so he picked one and from it he made a flute. Similar flutes have since been called the Pipes of Pan.

This story has remarkable similarities to the legend of the Giggleswick well. We do not know the name of the local satyr nor indeed do we know the identity of the nymph who was the object of his lust or urgent affections. But according to the story, the satyr had decided to impose his love upon the unfortunate girl and set out to catch her. She ran away to escape him, intent on maintaining her purity, and as she ran, she prayed to the gods for help. Eventually, she arrived at the point where the well now flows.

At that instant, her pleadings registered with the gods. They acted to save her – and turned her into a well. In a trice, the land produced a spring which has never stopped flowing with the purest of water and it was said that the ebbing and flowing was a reminder of the nymph's desperate panting as she fled from her pursuer.

In Pan's case, his victim ran into the water and was turned into a reed which made music, while the Giggleswick satyr's victim was turned into a well which still sighs in her memory. The similarities are interesting.

There is a wealth of folklore in this tale – we might substitute the devil for the satyr and St Alkelda for the nymph; we might also substitute an ordinary village girl and a local ne'er-do-well, but whatever the source of the story, it remains to give us reason to consider it and its antiquity. I can do little better than to quote now from a curious work called Polyolbion written by Michael Drayton (1573-1631):

> In all my spacious tract, let them so wise, survey
> My Ribble's rising banks, their worst, and let them say,
> At Giggleswick, where I a fountain can you show
> That eight times in a day is said to ebb and flow.
> Who sometime was a nymph, and in the mountains high
> Of Craven, whose blue heads for caps put on the sky,
> Amongst th'Oreads there, and Sylvans made abode
> (It was ere human foot upon those hills had trod),
> Of all the mountain kind, and, since she was most fair,
> It was a Satyr's chance to see her silvery hair
> Flow loosely at her back, as up a cliff she clambe,
> Her beauties noting well, her features and her frame.
> And after her he goes, which she did not espy,
> Before him like the wind the nimble nymph doth fly;
> They hurry down the rocks, o'er hill and dale they drive;
> To take her he doth strain, t'outstrip him she doth strive
> As one his kind that knew, and greatly feared his rape,
> And to the topicke gods by praying to escape,
> They turned her into a spring, which as she then did pant
> When wearied with her course her breath grew wondrous scant.
> Even as the fearful nymph, then thick and short did blow,
> Now made by them a spring, so doth she ebb and flow.

15   Grassington –

The Grassington Barguest

At the time of this next story, Grassington was known by its old name of Girston or Gerston, coming from the Celtic *garrs* or *gerrs* which were small fields or enclosures. Relics of that ancient name remain in the name of Garrs Lane. The Saxons certainly settled here, as did the Normans.

Today, this quaint and lovely old village is among the most popular of the Dales communities, both as a place to visit and as a centre for further exploration of the Pennine region. One argument which continues to ferment is whether Grassington is a town or a village. Travel writers insist on referring to it as a Dales village, but in fact it did qualify as a town as long ago as 1282 when it was granted a charter for a fair and a market. The fair lasted for three days over Michaelmas. Michaelmas Day is September 29th, and the fair was held on the eve, the day and the morrow of this feast day. There were sports such as chasing pigs whose tails had been covered in soap, sack-racing, sword-dancing, bull-baiting and badger-baiting, along with music, dancing, feasting and drinking.

A regular attender was a strange fiddler called Francis King who played several violins, each named after a woman. He would say that Peggy had broken her back, or he'd loaned Betsy to another musician, and that Polly was with him today …

This great fair was held until 1860, but did its termination mean that Grassington reverted to the status of a village? Indeed, the cobbled market place has been re-named The Square (which is triangular) and this would appear to suggest that all claims to be a town have been abandoned.

In addition to the fair, Grassington enjoyed some curious customs such as clock-dressing (when the town clock was decorated) and stang-riding. This was a penalty meted out to men who beat their wives; they were made to sit astride the stang, which was a long pole, and it was hoisted on to the shoulders of the others who then paraded the victim around the town when he was jeered and had filthy things thrown at him. Sometimes, a hen-pecked husband would be subjected to this treatment, but in Grassington a cart was used as a conveyance instead of the traditional pole or stang. In some parts of the country, nagging women were subjected to similar treatment known as skimmington-riding, but I have no record of this occurring at Grassington.

Another odd custom occurred at Grassington funerals. On the day of a funeral, chairs or trestles were placed outside the door of the house from which the coffin would be borne, and upon being brought out by the bearers, it was placed on those chairs or trestles. The mourners and friends then assembled around it, and a leader would then sing the first verse of a hymn. Others joined the remaining verses, singing them in a slow and respectful manner.

As the last line was reached, the coffin was hoisted on to the shoulders of the bearers and a solemn procession was then formed to convey it to Grassington parish church which in fact is located across the river at Linton. This is the beautiful church of St Michael and All Angels, well worth the short trip if only to see Linton Falls en route and the curious stone stile which crosses the church wall. Another custom was for pedestrians to uncover the head and lower the eyes as a funeral procession passed by.

Grassington occupies a beautiful setting some 700 feet (212 metres) above sea level in the shadow of the Pennines in upper Wharfedale. It has delightful cobbled streets, pretty stone cottages and interesting old buildings which reflect its role as one of the most important settlements of that area. There was an Iron Age settlement on the outskirts of the present town from 200 BC until AD 400, and this area was one of the most heavily populated at that time. In the middle ages, Grassington was very busy, with mining being its chief industry. During the reign of James I, miners were recruited from Derbyshire and worked for the private mine-owners of that time. There has been mining around Grassington for almost as long as the settlement has been in existence, and that includes a period as the main lead-mining centre of the Yorkshire Dales. Reminders of the industry, which dates from Roman times, can be seen all around the outskirts and also within the streets.

The railway came from Skipton in 1902 and with it some building of some new homes, but the Yorkshire Dales Railway, as it was known, was closed to passenger traffic in 1930.

Today, Grassington is a visitor attraction, although it first assumed this role as long ago as 1838. A writer called Frederick Montagu expressed an opinion that the mines were of interest, especially to the uninitiated and in 1869 the Reverend B.J. Harker wrote *Rambles in Upper Wharfedale* in which he recommended an underground trip in the old lead mines, even though the descent might be frightening to some! The mining era ended during the final years of the last century.

Today, Grassington is the location of the Yorkshire Dales National Park offices and other agencies such as the Upper Wharfedale Folk Museum and a Mountain Rescue Post, while a walk around the streets will reveal Grassington Old Hall dating to the thirteenth century, one of the oldest inhabited houses in the Dales. There are lots of interesting buildings in and around Grassington, ranging from one-time miners' homes which are now delightful Dales cottages to Theatre Cottage which was once a barn which served as a theatre run by Tom Airey, an eccentric who became postmaster at Grassington. He died in 1842. His theatre was good enough for the actor Edmund Kean who played here in 1807 before an audience of farmers and lead-miners.

Among the local actresses was a girl who was so poor that she could not afford to buy coal and relied for warmth on a thick red petticoat.

She was Harriet Mellon who became a very famous

actress, and who married the richest man in London, Thomas Coutts. She became the Duchess of St Albans. Neither she nor Kean were well known at that time, Kean acting under his real name which was either Carey or Carter.

Exploration of Grassington will reveal many points of interest, including an ancient footpath known as the Woggan and a right of way called Jakey, with various public buildings such as the Town Hall, once the Mechanics' Institute, an old Methodist church, a Congregationalist church, a primary school and a hydro-electric station. There are several *folds* in Grassington, this being the name for narrow lanes, many leading from The Square; these are called yards or ghauts in other Yorkshire towns. At one stage, Grassington was enclosed by gates to keep out domestic livestock which grazed on the fells.

One of the places of interest in the main street is the former smithy owned by Tom Lee during the eighteenth century. He was a blacksmith and owned the Blue Anchor Inn, now a butcher's shop. Lee achieved notoriety after murdering Doctor Petty and attempting to conceal the body – that tale is recounted in my *Murders and Mysteries of the Yorkshire Dales*, and that book also includes the strange story of a miner's death in one of the disused mines.

So far as folk stories of Grassington are concerned, there is one which does not feature in many earlier collections.

It is the story of the Grassington barguest and it appeared in the *Leeds Mercury Supplement* dated 28th February 1881. The account was in the broad Yorkshire dialect of the time, but I shall retell it in standard English.

We know that the storyteller was called Billy, but we do not know his surname, although it began with the letter B. He knew of the barguest and, in his own words, claims to have experienced a first-hand encounter with it – and survived.

Billy had been to Grassington one evening where he had joined his friends in one of the clock-dressing ceremonies. He had remained for some time after the ceremony and admitted that he had lingered longer than normal because he had enjoyed some glasses of ale with his pals. He states that he was not drunk and was aware of everything that occurred.

It was about eleven o'clock when he left Grassington to walk home and although it was the back end of the year (it would be St Michael's Day, September 29), it was a lovely clear night with a bright moon. He said he had never seen Rylstone Fell more plainly at night in all his life.

Then, in his own words, he said, 'I war passin' down t'mill loin, an' I heeard summat cum past me, brush, brush, brush, wi' chains rattlin', but I seed nowt … an' I thowt to mysen, now this is a most mortal queer thing.'

He stood still and watched, looking about himself, but saw nothing except the dry-stone walls behind the mill loin. Then he moved on.

The moment he moved, he heard again the distinctive noise, noting the brush, brush, brushing sound and the accompanying clanking of chains. Each time he stopped, the noise stopped. He noticed that when he moved, the noise resumed and then he thought it must be a barguest. There was a lot of talk about them and nearby was the infamous Trollers Gill barguest of Appletreewick and the Arncliffe barguest, so he knew what it was. He also knew that a barguest cannot cross water and so he hurried towards a bridge he knew, one built of wood.

But after he had crossed the bridge, he heard the thing again and thought it must have crossed after him, or else it had done a huge circular tour via Spring Head. But as that was almost a thirty-mile round trip, he discarded the idea. He realised that this barguest was able to cross water, if only via a wooden bridge. Now he was truly frightened for this was no ordinary barguest.

In his own words, he said, 'Now I became a valiant man,' and although he admits to being frightened, he did decide to try and catch a glimpse of the thing. He climbed the hill towards Linton and all the way was accompanied by the brush, brush, brush noise and the clanking of chains. Then, quite suddenly, it stopped. He also stopped and listened. There was no sound. He thought he had outwitted or lost the barguest and so he headed for home.

But he had hardly reached his door when he heard the noise again, once more being in the form of a brush,

brush, brush accompanied by clanking chains. As he was still being a valiant fellow, he left the safety of his own home and followed the sound towards Hollin House. Then, in the bright moonlight, he caught a glimpse of the creature's tail. In his own words, he said, 'Then, thowt I, thou awd thing! I can say I've seen thee now, so I'll away hame.'

But when he reached his own door for the second time, it had arrived before him. He described it as a huge great thing like a sheep, but bigger and more woolly, and it was lying across the threshold of his doorway. Billy was extremely valiant because he said 'Git up' and kicked it, but it wouldn't stir, so he kicked it again, shouting, 'Stir thyself', but it refused to move. And still being valiant, he raised a stick to 'baste it' as he writes, but then it looked into his eyes. He had never seen such eyes on an animal – they were like saucers with a cruel centre, and consisted of a red ring, a blue one and a white one. And as he watched, those rings grew smaller until they became a mere dot.

Now he was now more angry than terrified and kept shouting at it to move, saying, 'Git up and stir thyself'. But the massive creature refused.

But all his shouting had roused his wife who was in bed and she came to the door to find out what was causing the commotion. I now use his own words again, for he says, 'And t'wife heeard as how I were at t'door, an' she cum to oppen it, an' then this thing gat up an' walked off – for it war more fear'd o' t'wife than it war o' me!'

He called his wife to look at the departing creature and she agreed that it was a barguest. But neither Billy nor his wife ever saw it again – and each swore the story was true.

16   Kildwick –

The Kildwick Lions

Kildwick is in Airedale some four miles south of Skipton and sits astride the Leeds-Liverpool Canal. On its hillside site it remains surprisingly unspoilt even though it overlooks a busy meeting of main roads and some urban clutter.

One of its showpieces is a thirteenth-century stone bridge built by the Canons of Bolton Priory. The manor of Kildwick belonged to Bolton Priory and there is a record of the monks paying forty shillings and four pence for salmon and trout to be consumed at the funeral of Sir Robert de Stiveton or Steeton. He died in 1307 and is buried in the nave of Kildwick church.

Kildwick Grange was a residence of the prior of Bolton Priory although the present building is not the original, dating only to the seventeenth-century. Another historic building is Kildwick Hall. It stands on high ground above the village where it boasts extensive views across the dale. It is said to be a fine example of the architectural style used in seventeenth-century country houses or halls built in the Craven dales. There are many premises of this kind in the Craven dales and this fine building is now an hotel and restaurant.

Kildwick is a village of sturdy houses built in the dark stone of the region and it was voted the Best Kept Village in West Yorkshire in 1982.

Many of its houses overlook the slow-moving waters of the canal, so pretty at this point, but many lie below the level of its waters. A high aqueduct carries the canal over a road at one point.

One oddity is the curiously shaped church. Nicknamed the Long Church of Craven, it looks far too long for its width – it is 170 feet long but only 50 feet wide which gives it a strange elongated appearance. Inside, there are box pews with stone arcades that have no chancel arch to interrupt the view down the long building. Parts of the church date from Henry VIII and there is a fine Jacobean screen, as well as shields from the great families of the area such as the Cliffords and Plumptons. Portions of Saxon crosses remain, and the church boasts a letter written by Florence Nightingale in which she thanked people of Kildwick for their help in her work. Other oddments of interest include a 600-year-old key and a bassoon once played in the church! On the south wall is a sundial dated 1729 while the tower has a superb ornate clock.

The churchyard is fascinating. It is divided by the canal and one must cross a bridge to gain access to the higher parts, but the whole place is rich with distinctive tombstones. One of them, near the edge of the car park, marks the grave of the organ builder, John Laycock, who died in 1889 at the age of eighty-one. His memorial is unusual because it is a miniature copy of the very first organ that he built and is thought to be the only one of its kind in England.

But it is the ancient Kildwick Hall on the hill behind the village that has produced a curious legend. Its main gate is guarded by a pair of lifesize stone lions. It is said that when the lions hear the church clock strike twelve, they take a break from their eternal vigilance and walk down to the water's edge for a drink. They first reach the canal, and then the river …

While I was trying to find these lions, I asked a villager for directions and he told me – and added that when the lions hear the clock strike twelve, they descend for a drink …

It's nice to know that these old tales are still alive!

17 Leeds –

The Treasure of Kirkstall Abbey

For many visitors to the Dales, Kirkstall Abbey is a forgotten attraction. Many are unaware of its presence even though it stands close to the banks of the River Aire on the edge of Leeds. It is surrounded by the impedimenta of this thriving northern city instead of reclining at peace in the lush countryside of the Dales. Nonetheless, the abbey is beautiful and interesting and it is a credit to the city. Many Leeds people regard it as a haven of peace and solitude amid the bustle of the town.

Modern Leeds is a hectic place, the financial centre of the north and one of the leading business centres of Britain, and yet, scarcely more than a century ago the abbey was surrounded by charming villages, of which Kirkstall was one. With the city's rapid expansion, Kirkstall soon found itself surrounded by industrial buildings while the River Aire at this point became severely polluted with the effects of their presence.

In spite of this, Kirkstall Abbey has remained one of the best preserved of the Yorkshire monastic ruins and provides a remarkable contrast between the beauty of ancient times and the plain or even ugly appearance of contemporary buildings.

Kirkstall Abbey was founded by Henry de Lacy, although its predecessor was established in 1147 at Barnoldswick higher in the Dales. There were problems at the Barnoldswick site and during one of his journeys, Henry discovered an ideal replacement setting on the lush banks of the River Aire at Kirkstall. There was a small village here at that time; the prefix Kirk implies a church while 'stall' is indicative of small lodges in the centre of a large wood or forest. Building soon started and the monks moved into their new premises on 19 May 1152, the first abbot, Seleth, remaining in charge for the next thirty-five years.

As with all similar institutions, the fortunes of Kirkstall Abbey fluctuated widely; at times, it suffered grievously from debt, but then it became highly successful and affluent, albeit never reaching the status of near neighbours like Fountains and Rievaulx. And like so many, it was destroyed by King Henry VIII during his Reformation as a prelude to his founding of the Church of England. Today, Kirkstall's remains are exactly half-way between London and Edinburgh, being precisely two hundred miles from each.

From an archaeological aspect, the ruins are of constant interest, and it was during an inspection, many years ago, that a folk story was born. It happened long before the abbey was cared for in its present manner, and involved an experience by a Kirkstall countryman called Ralph Armitage.

He was mowing the long grass which grew in parts of the wastelands of the abbey, his intention being to make hay from it. It was a hot, sunny day and his work was arduous, so much so that frequent breaks for rest and refreshment were wise. Ralph broke for his 'bait' or 'snap', local names for a packed meal consisting of cheese and bread with some ale to wash it down. He settled near one of the surviving arches and as he ate, he gazed at the historic splendour around him. In the silence of the ruins, he was reminded of the legend which said the abbey contained buried treasure.

Like all the people of Kirkstall, he knew of the legend but had never been able to find the treasure; he knew, however, that it consisted of gold and silver coins, silver plate and other such valuables like chalices, jewelled crosses and croziers, all of which had been concealed moments before Henry's men had ransacked the abbey. All these were reputedly hidden in a chest and buried in vaults beneath the abbey ruins.

After his meal, Ralph lay down for a while, and in so doing stretched out and tried to find a comfortable place for his head. As he struggled for comfort, with his head at ground level, he noticed a curious hole deep among the fallen stones. He went for a closer look and, after moving aside some briars and stones, discovered a heavy door. There was no lock, so he opened it and found it led into a dark passage which contained a flight of stairs leading far below.

Among his possessions, he had a lantern in case he had to work late and so he lit it and ventured into this unknown passage. In all his life, even when playing in the ruins as a child, he had never come across this opening; it had been so safely concealed among the fallen masonry that it was pure chance that he now discovered it.

Deep below, at the foot of the stairs, he found that the passage opened into a large hall complete with a hearth and other doors, rather like the entrance to a mansion house. As his dim light revealed the extent of this odd place, he noticed a black horse standing in one corner; it was tied to a hook in the wall. Beside it on the floor stood a massive chest of oak. On top of that chest stood a fierce cockerel and the moment it saw Ralph, it started to crow loudly. He was tempted to run in case his unauthorised visit was discovered by someone else, but he paused long enough to realise that the chest must contain the famed treasure of Kirkstall Abbey.

Ralph was no coward and was determined to have a look, just to satisfy his curiosity. There seems to have been no wish to steal the treasure. With the cock crowing loudly at him, Ralph approached the big black chest and the moment he laid his hand on the hasp, the cock's crowing grew louder and then the horse began to whinny as it crashed its front feet on the ground. In spite of this, Ralph tried desperately to undo the lock, but it was encrusted with the dust and dirt of centuries.

And then, just as he had succeeded in loosening it, something unseen swooped over his head and caught him a glancing blow on the temple; he never knew what had hit him, but it knocked him unconscious. Later, he thought it must be some guardian bird or devil or something else …

Ralph fell into a deep unconsciousness and when he came to his senses, he was back in the grounds of the abbey, but lying in a different place. As he gathered his wits, he began to search once more for that elusive door into the undercroft, but he never again found it. And neither has anyone else.

The treasure of Kirkstall Abbey still awaits the person who can find that secret door.

18 Lothersdale –

The Swine Harrie

Lothersdale will be forever associated with Charlotte Bronte who, for a short time, was employed here. In June 1839 she was appointed governess to the Sidgwick family and worked in a large house called Stonegappe. It still stands, having been immortalised as 'Gateshead' in *Jane Eyre*. Charlotte was most unhappy here. Although she loved the house, its grounds and the surrounding countryside (she said the grounds were divine), she felt she was engaged in drudgery with no scope for mental freedom.

Her charges were Mathilda aged six and John Benson aged four, and she was made to do menial tasks like sewing and mending, even making dresses for the dolls. In addition, as governess to the Sidgwick children, she found she was not accepted by the servants because she was not of their social class, neither did she fit in with the family because she was not of their class either. She was lonely and felt rejected. For example, she was not allowed to eat with the other servants, nor was she allowed to eat with the family except on special occasions. As a consequence, she often ate alone in her room, her meals being reluctantly brought to her by one of the domestic servants.

To compound her misery, Mrs Sidgwick made her work like a slave and Charlotte found it impossible to keep order among the children – she called them 'unmanageable, perverse, riotous cubs'. The Sidgwicks, on the other hand, seemed to like Charlotte and took her away with them on holiday. They went to Swarcliffe Hall near Birstwith in Nidderdale, not far from Harrogate, but in spite of their efforts, she was never happy. She left Stonegappe in late July the same year, but her time at this Lothersdale house lives on in her classic novel, *Jane Eyre*.

Lothersdale has few other claims to fame; it is a far outpost of North Yorkshire, lying deep in the hills close to the Lancashire border on the west and the West Yorkshire boundary to the south. It lies on the route of the Pennine Way long-distance footpath as it runs south-to-north through Cowling, Lothersdale and then Thornton-in-Craven, and is situated in a triangle of fells between Barnoldswick, Keighley and Skipton. Its situation deep in the Pennines made it a refuge for Quakers during the reign of Charles II and for years its Friends' Meeting House was a place of pilgrimage for the faithful of that creed. Christchurch, consecrated in October 1838, a few months before Charlotte Bronte's arrival, stands on a hillside with far-reaching views across the surrounding fells, while the cottages, houses and mills straggle along a pretty stream which winds through the village before joining the River Aire between Skipton and Keighley.

Worsteds were made here during the last century by a family called Wilson whose millwheel was said to be the largest in the area.

A field in Lothersdale, on the side of Pinnow Hill, was for years known as Swine Harrie. This is the location of a folk story which has its counterpart in many other parts of Britain. The others usually involve a stone called either the Hangman Stone or Deadman's Stone, and tell of a thief who stole an animal like a sheep or a deer. In most cases, the thief carried the carcase home at night by slinging it around his shoulders and neck upon a length of rope. When he halted to rest, he placed the carcase on top of the stone but did not remove the rope from his own body. When the carcase slid to one side of the stone, he was unable to prevent its weight tightening the rope around his own neck as it slowly strangled him.

There are many variations of this tale – one such Hangman's Stone stands between Farndale and Hutton-le-Hole on the North York Moors where a man, who had stolen the carcase of a sheep, settled down for a rest. The sheep was tied to his shoulders with a rope, and as he sat down near the stone, the heavy carcase slid behind the slender upright and he could not retrieve it, and so he was strangled.

In the case of the Lothersdale Swine, a similar tale is told. A local man had decided to hunt and steal a pig, the local word for this being 'harrie'.

It means to chase with the view to stealing or plundering, and so the term 'Swine Harrie' refers to the place where such a theft occurred. The thief was crossing the field in question, with the swine at the end of a long rope, when he came to a high stone wall of the kind that enclose the land hereabouts.

Over the wall was a stile formed of two ladders, one at either side of the wall, with a small platform on top. The pig could not climb the ladder and so the thief was obliged to lift it on to the small platform before both could descend the other side. It was a heavy beast and the long rope was a nuisance, as well as being a danger during the climb. So the thief wrapped it around his own body to take up the slack and then lifted the protesting pig bodily into the air, intending to place it on the top of the twin ladders.

But in the darkness and confusion, the pig slipped from his arms and slithered down the far side; the rope unwound for a short distance, and then tightened itself around the man's neck. He could do nothing to free himself; he had no knife and could not lift up the pig from its place on the far side of the wall.

Next morning, a farm worker found them. Both the pig and the thief were dead, the rope having encircled the necks of each to strangle them.

The field has since been known as Swine Harrie.

19   Penhill –

The Giant of Penhill

As one drives along the A684 between Leyburn and Aysgarth in Wensleydale, the awesome bulk of Penhill looms above the southern slopes of the dale. It is one of the Pennines' lower range of fells, albeit a lofty mountain almost 1800 feet in height. It occupies a massive triangle of land between Bishopdale, Coverdale and Wensleydale.

The name is of interest because it is one of many which begin with the letters *pen*. Others include Penrith, Pendle Hill, Pendlebury, Pendleton, Penyghent and the Pennines themselves. The prefix *pen*, which appears in the Cornish tongue and the Welsh language, does refer to a hill, a mound, a height, a summit or even a head. For example, nearby Pen-y-ghent means a hill on a plain, ghent meaning a plain. Penhill is therefore an example of tautology because the name's literal interpretation becomes 'hill-hill'. Indeed, Pendle, over the border in Lancashire and famous for its witches, is a corruption of Penhill.

Because of its prime position overlooking much of Wensleydale, Penhill has witnessed a great deal of history. Upon its slopes, for example, are relics of Stone Age settlements, old wells and highways, and the remains of a chapel of the Knights Templar.

On one of the western slopes there is evidence of an old field system and the summit was once the site of a beacon. In the middle ages, a watch-tower was built on the hill and it was constructed in the style of a small castle. One old account quaintly describes it as a castlelet.

The entire mountain lends itself to legend and folklore and although several Dales stories are associated with the surrounding landscape, the mountain does possess its own dramatic story. Furthermore, below its northern slopes there lies the village of West Witton which, even today, practises a strange custom which has its origin in pagan times. It might even be associated with the story of the Penhill giant.

First, therefore, I will outline the West Witton custom which is known as The Burning of Old Bartle. Every year, on the Saturday night in August close to August 24, the day which brings Witton Feast to an end, the villagers carry the effigy of a man around the village until they reach a lane on the outskirts, and there the effigy is ceremonially burnt. The effigy is that of Old Bartle. As the procession moves around the village, it halts at several places to sing this rhyme:

In Penhill Crags he tore his rags,
At Hunter's Thorn he blew his horn,
At Capplebank Stee he brake his knee,
At Grisgill Beck he brake his neck,
At Wadham's End he couldn't fend,
At Grisgill End he made his end.

Each time it is chanted, a caller shouts 'Shout, lads, shout' and the people all loudly cheer 'Hip, hip, hooray'.

Due to the passage of time, probably many centuries, the purpose of this annual ritual has been lost. It may be significant that the village church is dedicated to St Bartholomew whose feast day is August 24 and whose name is often abbreviated to St Bartlemey or St Bartle. On the other hand, Baal, which can sound so like Bartle when spoken by some, was a sun deity in many civilisations, but the word also meant a lord or landowner. Perhaps the giant was Baal and perhaps the legend refers to the change from paganism and the worship of Baal, to the new faith? It seems illogical that a saint's effigy should be burnt in this way, so Bartle might not be St Bartholomew as some authorities believe, even though the event is so closely linked with his feast day. There are other links too, one being that St Bartholomew's Day has long been important in the rural calendar when many fairs and festivals of various kinds are held throughout Britain. Examples include the Horn Dance at Abbotts Bromley in Staffordshire, and the Blessing of the Mead in Cornwall. A good deal of weather lore is also associated with this date, such as 'St Bartholomew brings the dew' or 'As St Bartholomew's Day, so the whole autumn.'

Another theory about the Burning of Old Bartle is that the custom dates to pagan times when the last sheaf of the harvested corn was supposed to contain the corn-spirit.

The final sheaf was either preserved or burnt, depending on precisely where one lived. The corn spirit was associated with Ceres, the goddess of harvest.

Yet another theory, probably of more recent origin, is that Bartle was a horse-thief or sheep-stealer who is still receiving his punishment from the villagers. The latter tale may have been introduced in recent times in an attempt to explain the continuance of this odd practice. That tale says that Bartle was a noted thief of Wensleydale who had never been tempted to West Witton because the villagers threatened him with dire penalties if he dared to steal from them. But he could not keep away and came to raid their livestock; he was discovered and then chased around the dale, sometimes fleeing across the slopes of Penhill. In the flight for his life, he visited the other places mentioned in the old rhyme on page 113 after which he was caught and burnt to death. Ever since, so it is said, his treachery has been commemorated by the annual Burning of Old Bartle.

It is more probable, having read the story of the Penhill Giant, that the origins of this curious old custom are somehow linked with the tale of the giant who lived on Penhill. It might even be that Bartle and the giant are the same person, a focal point for differing practices told in a variety of folk tales. Each of them might have the same roots, all distantly associated with some ancient Norse folklore. Like Bartle, the giant of Penhill met his end through a fire.

He was not burnt to death, however, but it is not the purpose of this modest volume to explore that possibility. Instead, this is the story of the giant.

The date of the story cannot be accurately placed, but its roots are in pre-Christian times. The giant himself confirms that because, in the stories, he claims to be descended from the Norse god Thor. He lived in a mighty castle on Penhill and his only true friend was his dog, a boarhound called Wolfhead. There is no doubt that this was an extremely cruel giant with a warped sense of humour; he owned much of the land in the vicinity and had several tenant farmers working for him. But his chief source of pleasure was his herd of swine. He kept hundreds of them.

Every day, he would order Wolfhead to round up the pigs and drive them into his massive castle. As they passed through the gates, the giant would count them, meticulously checking that each was present and in good condition. He liked to see them growing fatter, for this meant their value was increasing and he was becoming richer. If one of his pigs had been harmed or become lame, or if one was missing, he went into a towering rage and rampaged across the countryside, ill-treating the people of Wensleydale and killing or stealing their livestock. He liked to savage the small flocks of sheep that were owned by the Dales farmers, sometimes setting his boarhound to attack and worry them. The local people tolerated this without turning against him, such was their fear.

But, simmering below the surface of their tolerance was a deep and burning hatred. It would not take much to release all fury. The opportunity came when the giant performed a deed far more cruel than any of his earlier ones. On this terrible day, he was striding through Yoredale, this being the old name for Wensleydale, when he noticed a small flock of sheep on the outskirts of a village. They were being cared for by a beautiful shepherdess called Gunda, and they belonged to her father. He was a simple man whose entire income came from his flock. Eager for a bit of sport, the giant ordered Wolfhead to round up the sheep, then urged the dog to attack them. This it did with its usual ferocity as the poor girl struggled to protect them; this provided amusement for the giant. He roared with laughter as the animals panicked and the girl rushed around in her efforts to save them, but the dog managed to seize one by the throat and promptly savaged it to death. Then it went for another – and another …

The distraught girl pleaded with the giant to end his awful game, saying her poor father had no other source of income, but the giant merely guffawed and encouraged the dog to greater efforts. For a time, the shepherdess ran around in a futile effort to save her sheep, but the combination of giant and dog was too much. Finally, she simply sat on a rock and wept as the destruction continued around her.

At this, the giant seems to have shown some compassion because he called off the dog and began to talk to the girl.

Unfortunately, his talk became rather too familiar and he began to make romantic advances towards her. At this, she fled. She ran towards the security of a nearby wood and her slender, light figure was swifter even than the giant with his enormous strides. Her rejection made him furious and as he could not catch her, he urged the dog to chase her. For a time, the terrified Gunda dodged both dog and giant, using the trees for protection and concealment, but the dog followed her scent and, time after time, flushed her from her hiding-place. In the end, tired and sobbing in her anguish, she tripped over a tree root and the dog was upon her. It began to savage her, biting into her throat and arms as she fought it off by using her bare hands and any sticks she could reach. Within seconds, her body and clothing were covered with blood. Meanwhile, the giant had heard the snarling and reached the scene.

At the very moment the giant arrived, Gunda managed to seize a large rock and, in a final desperate attempt to gain her freedom and win her life, she crashed it upon the dog's head. It burst the animal's nose and the angry dog fled, howling with pain. This so infuriated the giant that he lost his temper and with a tremendous effort, uprooted a small tree and used it as a club. He killed the unfortunate Gunda on the spot, then whistled for his dog. Both then returned to the castle.

This awful and unnecessary cruelty angered and

bewildered the local people and served only to increase their fear.

In abject sorrow, they buried poor Gunda in the village, never forgetting her ordeal, and for a time the giant continued his cruelties and savage behaviour. They seemed powerless to prevent him.

Then one morning, as Wolfhead was driving his swine into the castle for their daily check, the giant saw that one was missing. It was a particularly good animal, a fine boar which would bring him lots of money if he sold it, but it was nowhere to be seen. He ordered the dog to go into the hills to trace it. Off went Wolfhead, but he could not find the missing animal; the giant then ordered his swineherds to conduct a search, and they failed to locate it.

The giant decided to give the dog another chance. 'Seek,' he ordered. 'Seek till you find the missing boar! And do not dare come home until you have found it ...'

The giant failed to realise that poor old Wolfhead was ageing fast. The huge dog, who had been the giant's only true friend and who had served his master so well over the years, was now tired and feeble. To undertake a thorough search of those tough mountain slopes was almost impossible for the ageing dog, but he did try. And he was successful. After many tiring hours, he found the missing boar – but it was dead, with an arrow through its eye. Wolfhead sat beside the boar's corpse and began to howl.

His plaintive voice reached the sharp ears of his master who hurried to the scene.

When he saw the dead boar, his rage was intolerable. He kicked his faithful friend and beat him with a large branch, blaming the dog for the boar's death. Poor old Wolfhead slunk away as the giant's roars of anger shook the entire neighbourhood, somewhat like the tantrums of his ancestor, Thor. How dare anyone kill his prize boar? Who was the fiend? If he was ever found, he would have his hand cut off and then he would be slowly tortured until he died a miserable death ...

The giant slung the dead boar over his shoulder and carried it back to his castle where he summoned his steward and ordered him to travel into the villages and hamlets of Wensleydale. He had orders for every man and boy who was capable of shooting an arrow – they were to assemble on a high cliff on Penhill where each would be questioned about the dead boar.

The anguish among the people was enormous, for none knew who had killed the giant's prize animal and so they could not give a name, but they had no choice but to gather for questioning. Every one of them began the long walk to the cliff-top on Penhill.

Meanwhile, the giant realised that his only friend, his fine dog, Wolfhead, had not returned to the castle. Never before had the dog strayed and so the giant sent his men to seek the dog, but with no success. Wolfhead had vanished. The giant found himself waiting for his return with a mixture of anger and sorrow – what could have happened to Wolfhead?

Meanwhile the men and boys had assembled on Penhill and were awaiting him. The giant went to meet them; he was carrying the arrow which had killed his boar.

'Which of you fired this arrow?' he asked.

There was no reply.

'Some of you know the culprit,' he bellowed. 'You shall tell me his name.'

'No one knows …' ventured a brave spokesman.

'You shall not defy me,' thundered the giant. 'Go, all of you, go back to your villages and bring every child to this place. Gather them here at sunrise tomorrow, every one of them. When you see what I shall do to your children, then you will tell me the name of the man who killed my boar. Go! And by the great god Thor, some of you will speak!'

But before the men and boys had a chance to depart, a small wiry man with a long grey beard detached himself from the gathering and addressed the giant. He carried a long stick like a shepherd's crook and he showed no fear.

'What will you do to the children?' he asked gently.

'I have the power of life and death, greybeard,' snarled the giant. 'I will make these people speak – and I advise you to keep a civil tongue in your head, old man, whoever you are!'

'Is that your answer?' continued the old man.

'It is the only answer I will give, short of shooting an arrow from my own bow!'

'Then remember this,' the old man continued. 'Tomorrow is Thor's day and I warn you. I warn you that if you spill one drop of blood from just one child, or if any of those children cry out in pain or fear, then you will never again enter your castle, dead or alive. I speak of what I know, giant. Believe me.'

'Go away, you silly old fool,' snapped the giant. 'Why should I listen to you? You will see what happens tomorrow!'

One of his henchmen warned the giant that the old man was the famous Seer of Carperby, one who could foretell the future, but the giant dismissed his words as rubbish, then stormed back to his castle on Penhill. As the men and boys began to filter away, the Seer addressed them. 'Fear not tomorrow,' he smiled. 'All your babes will return unhurt. I promise you.'

Back at his castle, the giant enjoyed the spectacle of the men and boys slowly returning home with their awful news, and was chuckling to himself when he noticed his old dog lurking at the edge of the forest. He called out to Wolfhead, but, for the first time in his life, the dog disobeyed his master. He lay down and refused to move. This angered the giant so much that instead of going to see if his faithful friend was injured, he simply lifted his bow and despatched an arrow at the dog. It hit the faithful Wolfhead in the heart and he died instantly. Now rid of his old and now untrustworthy dog, the giant made his plans for tomorrow.

But that night, one of his old and most faithful servants came to the master and said, 'Master, I fear for your safety. I have noticed nine ravens flying over the castle and we all know they bode no good, they are a sign of impending death.'

'Death of those children, no doubt!' laughed the giant, who then struck the old servant about the head with his huge hand, sending him reeling to the floor. The man picked himself up and crept away to his quarters. But unlike the faithful dog, he was not dead. But he was very upset by his treatment.

That night, he went into the farm buildings of the castle and obtained nine battens of straw, nine armfuls of heather and nine baskets of peat. Under cover of darkness, he placed them in selected parts of the castle along with all the waste timber and rubbish he could find.

Next morning at sunrise, the giant strode off to the cliff on Penhill to meet the men with their children. They had gathered as ordered, many of them weeping with worry, but when he was only a few strides from his castle, he found a dead boar in his path, and then another. He soon found nine dead boars ... and then after striding nine more huge strides, he found a further nine dead boars ... his anger was mounting now, there would be no mercy for these villagers ...

By the time he reached the cliff-top he was in the foulest of moods, having found nine times nine boars, all dead, eighty-one of his finest pigs slaughtered by these people. Oh, how they would suffer ...

'You will all pay,' his voice thundered around the dale. 'Not only the babes, not only one man for every boar, but every living person. The blood of every one of you shall flow down the river; the Yore will be red with your blood for generation after generation ... the ravens shall feast on your bones and by the great god Thor, your villages will be burnt and there will not be a trace of any of you afterwards ...'

The men, cradling their babies in their arms, shrank away from this awful threat, but one man stepped forward. Once again, it was the Seer of Carperby.

'You dare to attend!' bellowed the giant. 'Here! Come to me if you dare!'

'I am no servant of yours,' said the gentle-voiced Seer. 'If you want to speak to me, then you must come to me! You are a braggard, nothing else.'

'You shall die before the others!' The giant's anger was at bursting point.

'Then first look behind you,' said the quiet bearded man.

Fearing a trick, the giant did not obey, but when the people all cried out in surprise, he turned his head. And there, on the summit of Penhill, his immense castle was on fire. Nine huge tongues of flame leapt from sections of the building and a massive pall of smoke was gathering over the hilltop. The castle was burning ferociously, fanned by the wind that is ever present on that exposed place, while his servants all fled for their lives.

For a moment the giant did not know what to do and then, in a fit of white fury, he advanced on the Seer with his axe raised high. The old man merely held up his hand to halt the mad giant. And then a curious thing happened. For some reason, the giant halted in his track and turned pale and dizzy, the axe fell from his hand and he began to shake all over. Trembling, unable to control his movements, he staggered backwards, edging nearer and nearer to the cliff-top ...

Only then did the gathered people realise what had caused the giant to behave like this, for they could see, framed against the blackened sky, the ghost of the murdered Gunda.

And beside her, tugging at a leash that she held, was the ghostly form of Wolfhead, his dead dog. The dog was straining to leap at his master, not out of love this time, but with a determination to avenge his own death ...

The giant shrank from this terrible sight, each step taking him closer to the edge of the cliff as everyone watched in fascinated horror. And as the giant teetered on the edge, Gunda released the spectral hound and it leapt at the giant's throat. The two of them hurtled over the edge of the cliff as Gunda disappeared. The ghost of Wolfhead was never seen again, but the giant of Penhill died that morning. Now, the people were free and the children were safe. And never since that time have the people of Wensleydale been troubled by descendants of Thor.

20   Pontefract –

The Origin of Pontefract Cakes

Pontefract is one of West Yorkshire's industrial towns and is located within a couple of miles of the junction between the A1 and M62. It is a busy mining-town on the edge of lower Airedale not far from Ferrybridge Cooling Towers, but has a surprisingly handsome racecourse and a castle which for centuries has featured in English history. Among its more dramatic events are the shockingly cruel death of Richard II and it was also the last royalist stronghold to capitulate during the Civil War. The town is also famous for its black liquorice sweets known as Pontefract Cakes whose origins are featured in a Yorkshire folk story.

The town's long and eventful history is worthy of record. Although Pontefract rarely features in modern histories or tourist information leaflets, it has been very prominent in the past for the castle is said to be one of the most strongly positioned in the country, occupying one of the finest of natural positions. Before the district became so industrialised and built up, Pontefract Castle guarded the routes into Airedale and Calderdale.

Long before this, Pontefract was the site of a Brigantian settlement and a Roman station, the manor of Pontefract being given to Ethelburga, wife of Edwin.

He was the first Christian king of Northumbria and the manor was then called Taddenescylf or Tateshale. It was here, in AD 946, that Eadred was acknowledged as King of Northumbria, and by the time of the Domesday Survey, Pontefract was known as Tateshall and in some Norman charters it was called Kirby, then a part of the manor of Tateshall or Tanshelf as it was sometimes spelt. After the Conquest, in 1080, it became the property of Ilbert de Lacy, upon whom William conferred huge areas of land in Yorkshire, Lincolnshire and Nottinghamshire, and it was the de Lacy family who built and nurtured Pontefract Castle into the formidable fortress that it soon became. The de Lacys occupied it for six generations until the last male member of the family, Henry, fell to his death from the battlements in 1310. It then passed to his daughter who married Thomas, the Earl of Lancaster, who was cousin of Edward II. The Earl of Lincoln occupied it for another four generations. At one stage it had at least eight towers and it had so many involvements with our history that it is not possible to include them here, although mention might be made of some of its tragic scenes. The Earl of Lancaster was beheaded here in 1322; Richard II was starved to death within its walls; Richard Neville, the first Earl of Salisbury, was beheaded here; the bodies of the Duke of York and the Earl of Rutland, killed in battle, were buried nearby; the future Richard III imprisoned and executed his enemies here and many other misdeeds occurred.

It seems the people of Pontefract hated the castle because of its evil associations and asked that it be demolished; in April 1649, permission was given and the castle was laid to ruin. Its remains can be seen today, and so a visit will now evoke but a small echo of its rousing past.

In addition to the castle, Pontefract had a wealth of churches and religious institutions, including houses of the black friars, the grey friars and the white monks. Most have disappeared. The splendid Moot Hall that once graced the market place has gone too, and its place is occupied by the town hall, an eighteenth-century building. Also in the market place is the Butter Cross dating to 1734, and an old water pump donated to the town by Elizabeth I after her visit to the castle.

There is history here, but today it must be sought among Pontefract's more industrialised frontage.

In bygone times, Pontefract had more than the usual

number of hospitals and almshouses, and close to one of them was an old cave reached by a descent of seventy-two steps wherein dwelt a hermit called Adam de Laythorp. He had laboriously carved both the cave and the steps to fashion his oratory in which he said Mass.

Around the town, there were once fertile fields which gave rise to market gardens and highly productive farmland, and today the town remains a curious mixture of things ancient and modern, clean and dirty, historic and worthless.

Locally, the town is still called Pomfret and some believe this to be its real name, but others claim it is merely a colloquialism. Nonetheless, the name is ancient with one writer claiming to have found about forty differing spellings and pronunciations. In official and ecclesiastical records, however, the name is usually given as Pontefract.

Some accounts suggest it received that name soon after the Normans arrived, about the time that Ilbert de Lacy began the construction of his castle. The name may imply a broken bridge, a bridge over the River Aire being demolished to frustrate the advance of the Normans. There was a town called Poumfreite in Normandy, and the name might have been brought from there, either by the Conquerer or by some of his nobles.

There is a record, in the fourteenth century, of the town being known as Pountfret when miracles were supposedly occurring at the tomb of the beheaded Thomas, the Earl of Lancaster. It was from the Cluniac Priory at Pontefract and in the reign of Edward III that a mission went to the Pope in Rome in an attempt to institute the canonisation process for Thomas. Money was collected to build his shrine on the site and it is said that in 1330 or 1389, St Thomas of Lancaster was declared a saint. However, his name does not appear in the Vatican's calendar of saints. Nonetheless, a hill near the castle, where the Earl was beheaded, did become known as St Thomas' Hill, although the Cluniac Priory where he was buried has vanished.

In 1828, the body of a very large man was found in a coffin in Priory Field, not far from St Thomas' Hill, and it was suggested this was the Earl's remains which had been removed from the Priory for safety during the Reformation.

Among all the claims to fame made by Pontefract, the best known today is the creation of the highly popular round black liquorice sweets known as Pontefract Cakes. The word liquorice comes from the Greek 'glycerhiza' meaning 'sweet root' and the plant is a native of southern Europe. It grows around the Mediterranean shores and was known in ancient times as a sweet plant with medicinal values; it is mentioned on the clay tablets of Babylon, and was used by the early Egyptians, Greeks and Romans as a medicine. It grows as a vegetable and is a graceful plant with feathery leaves and immensely long, thin roots, sometimes ten or twelve feet in length, but more usually between four and five feet long, but only around half an inch wide with many slender offshoots.

The roots are harvested, being at their best when the plant is some three years old, and they are crushed, ground and boiled to extract the juice from which liquorice is made. It is used in cough lozenges and similar preparations, and is useful in easing stomach problems. One of its prime areas of growth is Spain, and after a while, liquorice was imported from Spain; even now, some children refer to liquorice as 'Spanish'.

So how does this ancient Mediterranean plant come to be growing in industrial West Yorkshire?

One theory is that the Romans, who did settle in this area, brought the plant to England and cultivated it, knowing of its remarkable curative qualities. Another story is that it was introduced to the area by the Black Friars who cultivated it in and around Pontefract, and there is a stamp in existence, used for pressing the image of Pontefract Castle on to the round cakes, which dates to 1614. Yet another account says that a schoolmaster went from Pontefract to Spain in the sixteenth century and noticed the tall plants with their long, slender roots. He thought they would make excellent canes for beating wilful children at school and so brought a few samples home.

The use to which he put those samples is echoed in a second legend involving a schoolmaster. This says that a schoolmaster was walking one day on the Yorkshire coastline in 1588, around the time of the attack by the Spanish Armada, when he noticed some curious vegetables on the beach. They had long thin roots and had been washed ashore from a wrecked Spanish galleon.

Thinking they would be very useful for birching naughty children, he collected them and took them home. Soon he was using them at school to thrash children who misbehaved but one boy seized a sample and bit it hard to ease his cries of pain – and he found he liked the taste of the root.

His pals did likewise – and soon the boys were queueing up to be caned so they could chew bits that broke off the strange new cane. It wasn't long before the canes were worn out and the schoolmaster realised that there must be something special about the roots, so he planted some remnants which survived – and they sprouted. Soon, he had a crop of liquorice.

Whether that schoolmaster found his roots of liquorice in Spain or on the English coast makes little difference to the story, for it was the children who liked to chew the roots and it was they who discovered a new sweet.

From that time, liquorice flourished in the fertile ground around Pontefract and soon the familiar small round 'cakes' were being made. Their popularity led to other designs being produced for children – long sticks of liquorice were made, some were in the shape of clay pipes or boot laces, and soon there were other novelties including the famous liquorice allsorts made in Sheffield.

Every single item that was produced bore the stamped impression of a bird on the gate of Pontefract's famous castle. Originally, that bird was an owl which is featured on the coat of arms of the Saviles, while the modern design symbolises the old entrance to Pontefract castle.

So what is the truth? We do not know, although it is worth noting that the famous herbalist, Nicholas Culpeper, included liquorice in his book *The Complete Herbal* published in 1649.

He wrote 'Our English Liquorice rises up with divers woody stalks, whereon are set, at several distances, many narrow, long green leaves, set together on both sides of the stalk, and an odd one at the end, very well resembling a young ash tree.' He went on to say the flowers are like those of pea blossom but of a very pale blue colour, and that the roots run very deep into the ground. He said the juice of the root was most effectual, and best obtained by squeezing the roots between two rollers. Boiled in water, it makes a good drink for those with a dry cough or hoarseness, wheezing or shortness of breath, as well as for other disorders including diseases of the breasts, stomach, urine and even the eyes.

Today, our liquorice is imported from Poland and Russia, and the Pontefract fields have gone. But the story of its discovery as a sweet remains part of Pontefract's folklore.

21   Richmond –
Potter Thompson and the Drummer Boy

Richmond is full of history and the atmosphere of bygone days prevails in this beautiful old town. For centuries, it has dominated the lower reaches of Swaledale, so much so that the district is still called Richmondshire, and yet it is a small town with an astonishing sloping market-place and some delightful steep streets. Many are cobbled in the manner of times past. These quaint streets beg exploration, for they constantly provide memorable views and offer regular surprises, especially for first-time visitors.

Richmond lies a short distance to the west of the A1 near Scotch Corner, and is a few miles south of the A66 which stretches from Scotch Corner over Stainmore Forest and the Pennines into the Lake District. It is a wild, hilly but romantic setting, and as a centre for touring Swaledale, it is ideal. There are some good hotels, inns and shops in addition to its historic charms.

Its history dates from ancient times, with the castle continuing to dominate the town. Work on its construction began in 1071 by Earl Alan Rufus and a remarkable amount of Norman stonework remains, especially in its keep. Standing high on a massive rock overlooking the river, its tall keep rises above the rooftops of the town as it has for many centuries.

The views from within the castle are breathtaking and no visit to Richmond is complete without walking within these powerful walls. It is said that a treasure of gold lies deep beneath the Gold Hole Tower. The view from the battlements is marvellous, for they look across Swaledale and the cascading river below, and offer delightful vistas of the town's narrow streets, wynds and patches of greenery. The churches are all of interest and include St Mary's in Frenchgate with a porch and tower dating to the fifteenth century, St Joseph and Francis Xavier's Catholic church in Newbiggin with its beautiful oak altar in the Lady Chapel, and the curious church of Holy Trinity in the Market Place. This is surrounded by other buildings such as shops and offices which are now part of it and in recent times, it has performed many duties – it is now a regimental museum for the Green Howards.

The tiny Theatre Royal in Victoria Road is Georgian, dating to 1788, and is still in use while other sights include Friars' Wynd, Greyfriar's Tower and the ornate folly known as Culloden Tower. It was in Richmond at Hill House in Frenchgate that the song writer Leonard MacNally noticed a beautiful girl called Frances I'Anson; so impressed was he that he wrote a famous song in her honour. That was 'Sweet Lass of Richmond Hill'. Frances lived at Hill House, but died at the early age of twenty-nine.

Richmond's ancient history has given rise to some legends, one of which said that a bridge in the original town was constructed by the Devil. It seems that Satan was in need of rest and refreshment while exploring these dales and a good shepherd took him in and fed him. So grateful was Satan that he built a bridge across the Swale and that led to the creation of the community we now called Richmond. That is the legend, but the truth perhaps comes from clues in the town's name. It is thought to come from the Norman French meaning 'strong hill', perhaps a reference to the position of the castle whose presence resulted in the development of the town which surrounds it. It is doubtful whether there was a real community here before Rufus selected the site. It is said that when Rufus began work on his castle, he called it Richemond after a castle in Brittany of that name. Another theory is that the name comes from Ricesmund meaning a hill of rule, or government. Richmond in Surrey is named after the Swaledale Richmond.

It is the castle which provides the setting for two

oft-repeated folk tales. One concerns the famous underground discovery by a simple chap called Potter Thompson, while the second is the sad and mysterious story of a young drummer boy who attempted to follow in Potter's footsteps.

The basis of the first legend is similar to many throughout England because it is said that King Arthur and his Knights of the Round Table sleep somewhere deep beneath Richmond Castle, awaiting the time when England needs their services. They did operate in the Yorkshire Dales and it is claimed that Arthur's last battle was either at Catterick or on the slopes of the Eston Hills, now in Cleveland.

Unlike most of the Arthurian 'slumbering knights' tales, the Richmond one has a secondary element, the famous sword Excalibur.

Potter Thompson was a simple and rather timid soul who lived and worked in Richmond and it seems he had a nagging wife. She never praised him or thanked him, but subjected him to a constant barrage of complaints and verbal abuse. She said he was idle, feckless, useless and no good to anyone. The poor fellow could never do anything right. The result was that Potter spent a lot of time wandering the streets of Richmond or meeting his pals in the ale-houses. This served only to increase her nagging, but he saw little alternative.

After a particularly rousing bout of nagging, Potter went for a long walk and found himself exploring the shrub-covered banks on the riverside below the castle walls. He had often been here, especially as a child, when he would explore the area and make dens. He loved the countryside around the Swale where the solitude suited his quiet nature and somewhat timid attitude.

On this day, he was alone, now a mature man who knew every inch of the town and its environs. But on this occasion, he noticed a cleft in the huge rocks upon which the castle was built. It lay behind some bushes and he thought the bushes must have wilted or died to reveal this large opening. Most certainly he had never seen it during any of his previous visits and it intrigued him. He wanted to know more about it.

Being full of curiosity, Potter decided to have a look inside; it was large enough for a small man to squeeze into and once inside, he found it opened into a larger tunnel where his movement was easier. And there was a strange grey light inside too; its source appeared to be a long way inside.

Potter, although a simple man, had heard the legend of Richmond Castle, but it is also likely he had listened to tales of buried treasure and that he wondered if he was to become a wealthy man. Maybe his sudden wealth would stop his wife from nagging? It was worthy of some effort, he decided, and so he continued, somewhat nervously, along this dark passage which was leading into the depths of the earth below the castle. And as he walked deeper into the bowels of the earth, so the light grew brighter and suddenly, as he turned a corner, he found himself within a huge underground chamber. He was tempted to turn and flee, but managed to calm himself long enough to examine his surroundings.

Before him was an astonishing sight.

The first thing that caught his eye was the bright lantern hanging from the ceiling and casting an intense light over everything, and then, glistening in that light, he noticed a jewelled sword lying in a scabbard on a large stone table. That scabbard was also adorned with many jewels which glistened as he halted to admire this amazing scene. Also on the table was a large horn encrusted with gold and silver; it had a silver chain attached and the ends were tipped with silver.

There were other riches, far too numerous to comprehend, and Potter realised that, at long last, here was wealth of the kind he had never imagined. The stories were true, after all.

But as he grew accustomed to the light, he saw much more. Lying around the edge of this huge circular chamber on beds of rough straw and blankets, were several very large men, all dressed in armour and resting in the deepest of sleeps. All were breathing very slowly and deeply, and all had a sword at the right hand, ready for instant action. One of them lay apart from the others and beside his rough bed was a crown embellished with splendid gold workings and precious jewels.

Potter was breathless and his nerves were now at a very high pitch, but what on earth was he witnessing? He knew the astonishing answer – he knew the legend of King Arthur was true. Even as a schoolboy, he had been told that King Arthur and his Knights of the Round Table slept below Richmond Castle, in constant readiness to defend their country, and here they were, all of them.

Every one was lying asleep and breathing with the sighs of those in very deep slumbers. Potter was astonished; he knew that many of the local people had refused to believe the story, but here it was, before him. It was true. He had to tell someone; he had to tell his wife that he had been honoured in this way …

Now Potter was not a dishonest man and had no intention of stealing from King Arthur, but he did realise that if his tale was to be believed, he would require some proof. The sword would be ideal – after all, what better proof could there be than the famous sword Excalibur? If he could remove it from its scabbard and show it to his wife and friends, then his story would be accepted as genuine – and so would his part in its discovery.

Silently upon the dusty floor, Potter tip-toed across to the huge stone table, first picking up the magnificent horn to examine it. But as he moved it, some of the knights stirred in their sleep, turning over and sighing. He almost ran from the room, so nervous was he, and so he hurriedly replaced it. But he must have that sword …

He knew that this was the most famous sword in the land, a magic sword in fact – and in spite of his nervousness, he seized it firmly. He intended to draw it from its scabbard. His heart was pounding by this time, and when the heavy sword moved, the sleeping knights stirred once more, this time with increased activity.

The huge cavern was filled with the noise of their armour clanking and moving as they began to rise from their beds. Some of them were groaning as they were aroused and all this was too much for Potter Thompson. He thrust the sword back into its scabbard and ran for his life. He ran as if all the devils in hell were chasing him, and as he ran, there was the sound of a great wind. It made him run all the faster … he was not to know it was the sound of the knights returning to their deepest slumber and sighing as they settled down yet again.

Terrified, poor Potter ran for the exit, and as he did so, he heard a disembodied voice calling:

> Potter Thompson, Potter Thompson,
> If thou hadst either drawn
> That sword, or blown the horn,
> Thou wouldst have been the luckiest man
> That ever yet was born.

Even as these words were being spoken, he was so frightened that he did not heed them and ran until he was out of the tunnel. With an immense feeling of relief, he squeezed through the crack in the rock until he was standing once again in the bright fresh air below the castle on the banks of the rippling Swale. His poor heart was still pounding several minutes later as he sat down to regain his breath and his composure. Potter sat for a long time, recovering from his experience, and he had to decide what to do next.

But as he pondered, those curious words came back into his mind. They went round and round in his head, repeating themselves time and time again, until he knew he should have either blown the horn or drawn the sword to its full length. Then he realised he *could* go back! If those words were true, he could do it all over again, right now, and then he *would* have proof! He could show his wife and the whole town … and he would have the luck promised in the verse.

Potter got to his feet, now calm and very determined not to be frightened again. But he could not find the entrance. He searched the entire area below the castle, pushing aside briars, shrubs and thick weeds, but the fissure in the rock could not be found. To the end of his life, no one would believe he had been into the chamber of the sleeping knights, and he spent all his spare time searching for the entrance that only he knew was there. But he never found it. There was no second chance for Potter Thompson.

The second story involves the same legend, but has a completely different ending. Among those who knew of the cave of King Arthur were members of a regiment of soldiers based at the castle. They knew that, somewhere beneath their feet, lay the secret cave, and they had also been told stories of a secret tunnel which led from Richmond Castle to Easby Abbey, about a mile to the south east of the town.

Stories of that tunnel continue today, but no one has ever proved that it existed – but no one has disproved the story either.

The soldiers, working as a group, did find some deep cellars and dungeons far below the keep of the castle, and decided that they should be explored. Perhaps one of them had a secret opening which led into King Arthur's chamber? Or perhaps concealed in one of them was the entrance to the secret tunnel leading to Easby Abbey? During their scrutiny of the castle's interior, they had found a tiny entrance which might be the one they sought.

Not one of them, however, was brave enough to enter the dark hole, and they suddenly realised that their tiny drummer boy would be able to squeeze through. They went to find him and offered him lots of money and good things if he would do them a favour – in his childish innocence, he agreed. They said they would equip him with a lantern and some food, and he had to explore the tunnel whose entrance they'd found deep inside the cellars. He must find out where it went. They explained it might lead into King Arthur's chamber in which case the drummer boy would become the luckiest lad alive if he drew the sword or blew the horn, or it might lead to Easby Abbey or it might emerge somewhere else. No one knew. If he found out, he would make history and become famous.

The gallant drummer boy agreed to this task. He would follow the route of the secret tunnel, and the soldiers told him to take his drum, and to keep beating it so that they could monitor his progress underground. And so, being very brave, the young drummer boy, only twelve years old, did as they wished. Deep in the cellar of the castle, they showed him the entrance and once inside the narrow, dark tunnel, he began to beat his drum. They could hear the rhythmic rat-a-tat-tat, rat-a-tat-tat as he moved slowly along the dark route. The soldiers returned to the daylight at ground level, leaving him to find his way.

They could hear the drum beat as the boy made his way through the tunnel, and it never stopped. Day after day, the rat-a-tat-tat of his drum could be heard below the surface of Richmond, sometimes down by the river, sometimes heading towards Easby Abbey, sometimes high in the town ...

And to this day, the drummer boy has not returned. No one else would search for him, and the soldiers were too large and heavy to squeeze into the narrow opening in the cellar. And so he is still down there, beating his drum.

It is said that if you walk in certain parts of Richmond in the very quiet times of night or early morning, you can hear the faint rat-a-tat-tat, rat-a-tat-tat of a drum-beat far below the ground as the lost drummer boy continues his important duty.

22   Rokeby –

The Felon Sow

For centuries, Rokeby lay within the North Riding of Yorkshire. Its position on the southern banks of the River Tees ensured its association with the Dales but when the local authority boundaries changed in 1974, Rokeby found itself in the newly created administrative County of Durham. Nonetheless, its ancient history and its story of the Felon Sow still belong to Yorkshire and so it is included within these pages.

The beauty of Rokeby's setting and its long, romantic history are all chronicled by Sir Walter Scott in his romantic ballad called *Rokeby*. He was a regular visitor and a close friend of John B. Morritt, the owner. Morritt, a noted patron of art and literature, was introduced to Sir Walter Scott in 1808 and the two men became close friends, visiting each other's homes over many years. Morritt was the only Englishman to know the secret of Scott's authorship of *Waverley*. Scott, in his diary of 30 May 1826, said of Morritt, 'He is one of my oldest, and, I believe, one of my sincerest friends – a man unequalled in the mixture of sound good sense, high literary cultivation and the kindest, sweetest temper that ever graced a human bosom.'

Morritt was also a friend of Southey the poet, and his family owned (and still own) the estate at Rokeby.

But Rokeby is not a village. It comprises a magnificent country house set in acres of lush parkland beside the River Tees a few miles to the south-east of Barnard Castle. The former Roman road, the A66 from Scotch Corner to

Bowes, passes by, from which drivers may catch sight of the splendid Palladian style house behind a high wall which borders the park. The house is open to the public and there are lovely walks in this area. Scott, writing to a friend called George Ellis about Rokeby, said, 'It is one of the most enviable places I have ever seen, as it unites the richness and luxuriance of English vegetation with the romantic variety of glen, torrent and copse, which dignifies our northern scenery.'

Here too is the delightful River Greta which enters the Tees near Rokeby Hall at a point known as The Meeting of the Waters. The area is rich with artistic and literary associations. Both Cotman and Turner painted this scenery, and in addition to Scott's love of the area, Dickens also came to undertake research for *Nicholas Nickleby* and *Master Humphrey's Clock*. On the night of 31 January 1838, after a rough coach journey of over 255 miles in cold, freezing conditions, Dickens and his friend, Hablot K. Browne (known as Phiz), found an inn with a roaring fire where they were given a huge supper and a bottle of mulled port.

These they enjoyed in a room with a fire half way up the chimney. This was the George Inn at Greta Bridge which is now a private house called Thorpe Grange.

It is the River Greta which gives its name to Greta Bridge, a village beside the A66, and Dickens was also to visit Bowes and Barnard Castle in his quest for the background to his work. There is ancient history here too; there was a Roman camp at Greta, established by Severus in the third century, and Scott described it as having a triple ditch with three entrances. But the Morrits' links with Rokeby began in 1769 when John Sawrey Morritt bought the estate from its builder, Sir Thomas Robinson; earlier, Robinson's ancestors had purchased the ancient manor of Rokeby from the family of that name. The Rokeby family, or Rokesbys as they were sometimes known, had owned the estate since the time of the Norman Conquest and the correct pronunciation is 'Rookby'. The family was prominent in the history of England until the time of Charles I when the estate passed to the Robinsons.

John B. Morritt was the son of John S. Morritt, the purchaser of Rokeby. In addition to his love of art and literature, John S. Morritt was a serious collector of some note; for example, he acquired the renowned painting by Velasquez called *The Rokeby Venus*, now in the National Gallery, and the house is rich with paintings, sculptures and architectural features.

The fame of Rokeby began when Scott published his poem of that name because it was the equivalent of a modern bestseller and drew the crowds to visit the area. Scott came several times during the writing of his poem, working in the open air on a seat in the park. Another of his favourite working-places was a cavern in the grounds overlooking the River Greta; it was called Bertran's Cave which became a type of study. Working here, Scott even noted details of the wild flowers and herbs that grew nearby in his search for complete authenticity, and it is thought this is the cave called the Robbers' Cave in Scott's poem. Scott took immense care to get his facts correct and when his poem became such a success, Morritt jokingly said he would punish Scott for making his home so well known to the public. One of his actions was to increase the rent of the inn which he owned in Greta Bridge – this was the Morritt Arms which did benefit from the tourists who came by the coachload.

One of the features given prominence by Scott was the fourteenth-century Mortham Tower which stands near the banks of the Greta not far from the Dairy Bridge and the Meeting of the Waters. There was the story of a ghost who haunted the underside of Dairy Bridge; she was called the Mortham Dobby and was a headless lady dressed in white silk which trailed behind as she floated about her hauntings. A priest exorcised her and confined her spirit to an arch of the bridge, but when the arch was damaged by flood waters, the spirit was released.

The Dobby resumed its hauntings, resorting to a part of the tower itself. It was said to be the ghost of a woman who was murdered on the banks of the river, after which her body was carried into Mortham Tower. Thereafter she haunted the Tower. Occupying a corner site in a small courtyard, Mortham Tower is a genuine peel tower and not a folly. Parts were added in Tudor times. With elegant battlements, it is thought that a Great Hall once existed too, but that has disappeared.

It is reputedly the work of the Baron of Rokeby who built it when the raiding Scots destroyed his home, and the family is said to have lived here when they suffered in their hard times. The stonework contains a coat of arms of the Rokebys, and the stairs are said to be stained with the blood of the woman whose body was carried here by her killer after she was murdered on the banks of the Greta. In addition to her bridge hauntings, the Mortham Dobby was said to haunt the tower until alterations removed the portion of the building where her body had lain.

Another point of interest near Rokeby is the small church, consecrated in 1778, which is outside the park beside the road to Bowes, a former Roman road. Scott's friend, John S. Morritt, and his wife are buried here. The chancel was added some ninety years after its foundation. Between here and Barnard Castle there are the ruins of Egglestone Abbey too, a former Premonstratensian house.

The enduring legend of Rokeby has all the elements of a comic farce, however, which makes a welcome change from the more dismal of our folk stories. It concerns a massive pig which had a mind of its own, so much so that it was known as the Felon Sow. The word felon was used to denote a person who had committed a serious crime like murder, robbery or rape, but an older meaning included something or someone who was wicked or cruel. It seems that the original teller of this tale thought the sow was wicked!

The story dates from the end of the fifteenth century and first appeared in print when Whitaker included it in his 'History of Craven'. It tells of a rogue sow. She was one of a herd of pigs kept by Baron Ralph de Rokeby, but this was a huge beast. She was known to be a savage animal, one which would cheerfully attack humans if they crossed her path, and she roamed the woods and parkland of Rokeby, almost at will. She went where she pleased and when she pleased. She was dangerous to man and beast, and was reputed to have killed several swineherds. This is a description:

> She was mare than the other three,
> The grisliest beast that e'er might be,
> Her head was great and grey,
> She was bred in Rokeby wood,
> There were few that thither goed,
> That came on lyve away.
> Her walk was endlong Greta side,
> There was no man that durst her bide,
> That was frae heaven to tell,
> Nor never man that had that might,
> That ever durst come in her sight,
> Her force it was so fell.

From all accounts, it seems that Ralph de Rokeby did not know what to do with his sow. No one could approach her so he could not kill her or use her for food, and all attempts at breeding from her had failed.

Then, for reasons which are open to debate, he decided he would donate her to the Grey Friars of Richmond. Their tower still stands to remind us of their former presence in the town, but we do not know whether Ralph was feeling very generous or whether he had a sense of humour because there was one important condition to this gift. He said that although the sow would not cost them any money, the monks had to come themselves to take her away. That was his condition. The old poem says that Ralph was 'full of good wille' when he made his offer, but in view of what happened, there is some doubt.

However, he knew the monks' larder was not very well stocked and assured the abbot that the sow was ready for collection. The abbot thanked him and offered to send a monk to Rokeby to fetch the sow. Friar Middleton was selected and it seems he did anticipate some trouble because he sought the assistance of two lay brothers, Peter Dale and Brian Metcalfe.

Off they went to Rokeby to bring the pig to Richmond, a walk of about ten miles. They intended to fetch her in the usual manner, with a rope tied to one leg and a stick to guide her forward along the route. It was the traditional, well-tested method.

According to the old poem, they found her 'liggan under a tree' beside the River Greta and they were astonished and somewhat fearful when they saw her. She was monstrous with beady eyes which never left them as they made their approach. She had grizzly rust-coloured hair and enormous teeth.

And when they walked towards her, the sow slowly got to her feet and without warning, charged at the men. They fled, taking shelter behind some trees, but they were not going to abandon their mission. There were three of them, but only one sow, and so they tried everything they knew as they attempted to get a rope around either leg or her neck. There followed something of a comic scene, with the pig chasing the men around the trees or into the river as they tried to lasso her. It seems they fell into briars, shinned up trees to escape her and generally experienced something not at all in keeping with their holy calling. Then for some reason, the sow got herself stuck in a kiln in the woods – during the chase, she had backed away from the monks and had wedged herself temporarily in this kiln. It enabled them to fashion a noose which they threw over her neck. Delighted at their success, they started to haul her out. At that stage, the sow appeared to have calmed somewhat because she walked out in a most docile manner with the halter around her thick neck, but it was all a pretext. The moment she was out of the kiln, she charged at them all. She managed to seize one of the lay brothers by the leg, inflicting a nasty bite wound in the flesh of his calves; she snapped and squealed as she chased another into some briars where he fell in an entanglement of prickly branches. She charged into him, butting him with her heavy head and sending him breathless into the thicket to suffer severe bruising and fear.

At this point, she turned her attentions to Friar Middleton. It seems that he realised he was no match for the determined sow and he fled, but she gave chase and he took the only escape route he could find – a convenient sycamore tree into which he climbed, or perhaps leapt, with a remarkable show of agility. The outcome was three very chastened holy men, one gored, one butted and one stuck up a tree as the ferocious sow patrolled her territory, squealing in a mixture of anger and delight.

As she watched her three adversaries, her sharp, dark and beady eyes ranging from one to another, she dared them to make more moves. None dared risk another sortie to capture her and so she stood there, guarding the sorry trio. Eventually, it was Friar Middleton who produced what he considered the solution to their dilemma. He was the senior man, in fact the only one who had been ordained in Holy Orders.

He believed that sow did not realise who they were. She thought they were ordinary men, men who worked on farms and dealt with animals in the course of their duties. She regarded them as just another bunch of swineherds who had come to trouble her. But, the friar reasoned, these were holy men, men of stature who should never be subjected to such treatment, even by an angry sow. He recalled the powers of St Cuthbert who could charm the birds on Holy Island, and the ability of St Francis of Assisi to communicate with wild creatures. Friar Middleton decided to inform the sow of his stature as a monk and so came down the tree and began to lecture the angry animal.

He prayed, using the Latin to quote from the Gospel According to St John, Latin then being the language of his church, but, as the old poem says, the pig 'wold no Latin verse' and simply squealed her anger and charged him once again. He took to the trees for a second time as the victorious pig galloped off, heading back to the peace of the riverside which was her home.

Somewhat chastened, the three brethren gathered themselves together and decided they were incapable of securing the violent sow and so returned to their monastery at Richmond without the pig. There they told their sad story and so the reputation of the felon sow was ensured. But the abbot was not amused and he was not to be defeated.

He had been promised the sow for his larder and was determined to secure it. He therefore commissioned two local fighting men, two champions of the battlefield, to go and fetch it. These were not monks, however; one was called Gilbert Griffiths and he was one of the most famous men-at-arms in the north of England, and for his companion, the abbot chose a Spaniard living in

Richmond who had fought and beaten the Saracens. This formidable team therefore sallied forth to Rokeby, fully armed and equipped with their finest weapons, to do battle with the felon sow.

We are not given many details of their war against the pig, but they did win. The old poem says of Gilbert:

All with force, he felled her there,
And won her worthily in war
And held her, him alone.

It seems that it was Gilbert who delivered the final blow and so he carried the sow back to the monks in Richmond, having cut her into two portions, one for each of the stout wooden panniers borne by his horse. As the final verse says,

And to Richmond anon
He brought her.
When they saw her come,
They sang merrily Te Deum,
The friars, every one.

One can imagine the monks singing Te Deum laudamus which means 'We praise Thee, O God' as they tucked into a breakfast of finest pork. Although their home has vanished, except for Grey Friars Tower in Richmond, the story of their final conquest of the Felon Sow of Rokeby lives on.

23 Rylstone –

The White Doe

Among the more enduring stories from the Dales is that of the famous White Doe of Rylstone. Maybe this tale is another which owes its survival to William Wordsworth, for he chronicled this lovely legend. Perhaps it would have endured without his welcome contribution, but the story remains as fresh and as intriguing as ever.

I visited Rylstone on a warm but foggy day and although the skyline was obliterated by the dense cloud, this small community lost none of its attraction. Ducks were swimming on the pond, we could just discern the cross on the hilltop which is a landmark for miles around while the church stands above the houses on its own lofty hillside. There are commanding views from the church, and some claim that this offers the finest view in the Dales, or even in the whole of Yorkshire.

Rylstone is a tiny collection of houses which lies roughly half-way between Grassington and Skipton on the B6265, this route being one of the oldest out of Skipton. There is a pleasant drive along this undulating route, for the bulk of Rylstone Fell, with its two distinctive mounds, lies to the east of the highway with the distant Pennines rising high to the west beyond Flasby Fell. High on Rylstone Fell is Upper Barden Reservoir while still further to the east lie some beautiful reaches of Wharfedale around Bolton Priory.

This is romantic country rich with history and accounts of stirring and daring deeds, for Rylstone was the home of the Norton family, since immortalised by Wordsworth due to their epic struggle for their religion. Richard Norton was the white-haired old father who encouraged his nine sons to become skilled at archery and the martial arts, and he maintained a hunting lodge on Rylstone Fell where his sons practised their craft. He had a daughter too, named Emily.

The remains of Norton Tower are on a hill about a mile to the south of Rylstone, now known as Norton Tower Hill; once, there were traces of a long wall here, and the outline of a pound used by the Nortons for enclosing their red deer. Years ago, the family were involved in a legal dispute against the Cliffords, also a land-owning family, over the right to take deer in this area. Evidence was produced that 'old ladye Clifford had been seen to hound her greyhounds within the said ground at Rylstone' but the outcome of the case is not known.

It is Francis Norton who features in Wordsworth's long work. According to the poet, Francis was the only male Norton who did not take part in the Rising of the North but he was murdered and lies buried at Bolton Priory. It was his death and the actions of his sister which led to the story of the white doe.

The Nortons were staunch Catholics, and remained fervent supporters of that religion during the dark days of the Reformation.

While the English establishment was doing its best to crush the Catholic faith and to remove all evidence of its history in this land, the Nortons, with the exception of Francis (the eldest), joined other landowners in the ill-fated 'Pilgrimage of Grace'. Francis advised caution in such matters, but a year later, a second rebellion known as the Rising of the North involved several members of the aristocracy under the leadership of the Earls of Northumberland and Westmorland; its aim was to restore the Catholic faith to England after it had been outlawed, and its members protested against the destruction of the Catholic abbeys and monasteries by Henry VIII. The attempt failed and the newly formed Church of England survived to become the State religion, but nine Nortons – father and eight sons without Francis – were arrested and conveyed to

Barnard Castle, when they were tried and condemned to die at York.

> 'Thee, Norton, wi' thine eight good sons,
> They doom'd to dye, alas for ruth;
> Thy reverend lockes thee could not save,
> Nor them their fair and blooming youthe.'

Although sentenced to death, not all of them died; Thomas and Christopher, however, were executed, but the others survived although the entire Yorkshire estate was confiscated and handed over to the Crown. For Christopher's role in the escape of Mary Queen of Scots, see 'Castle Bolton'.

Adherence to their faith cost them everything. Francis, however, who had not joined his family in the plot, survived and managed to snatch the banner from the men whose actions had led to his father's and brothers' deaths. He took this home with him, but as he was passing Bolton Priory, he was caught by Sir George Bowes and his horsemen. Francis was murdered and later buried at Bolton Priory. Years later, the Crown released the estate and eventually it fell into the hands of the Cliffords, royal favourites who later became the Earls of Cumberland. The only survivor in this country was Emily.

Wordsworth referred to the Nortons' home as 'Rylstone's old sequestered hall', and very little evidence of it now remains – it stood to the east of the church and I believe some of its ancient stones now form part of Rylstone church. This was rebuilt during the last century, although there are some medieval crosses in the churchyard and some Norman fragments around the premises. Around the turn of this century, the site was covered with sycamore trees. Nearby was a Vivery, the name given to a pleasure ground comprising topiary works, fishponds and an island, all linked to the hall.

Alone in the world, Emily was considered rather a saintly girl, one who could communicate with animals, and as a child she had made a pet of a white doe. The baby deer had followed Emily everywhere like a dog, but as it grew she released it into the wild. From time to time, she saw it with the herd in the park, but it never resumed its domestic role.

Later, when her father and brothers had been executed, she would walk over to Bolton Priory where they were buried, being especially careful to visit Francis' tomb, and there she would pray for their souls. It was that action that led to the legend of the white doe of Rylstone.

According to legend, Emily clung to the Catholic faith and wandered the fells, staying at remote cottages with trusty friends and living the life of a nomad. One of her favourites was a miller's cottage near Linton and her visits are still commemorated in a small, single-arch bridge. It stands close to where Threshfield Beck joins Linton Beck before entering the Wharfe, and it is affectionately known as Lile Emily's Bridge. Lile means little or small, but the term is used more as one of affection than one which indicates her physical size.

During those awful times of rejection, and as a respite from her wanderings, Emily decided to visit her old home at Rylstone and walked across the fells, full of anticipation, eagerness and joy. As she rested beneath a fine oak in her former park, she became aware of a herd of deer grazing at a distance and among them was a white one, a beautiful, elegant doe. Then it saw her. It detached itself from the herd and came slowly towards her, its big eyes watching the girl beneath the tree, until at last it reached her.

Then it settled at her side and placed its head in her lap as it gazed into her face, full of trust. As Wordsworth said,

> The pleading look the lady viewed,
> And, by her gushing thoughts subdued,
> She melted into tears –
> A flood of tears that flowed apace,
> Upon the happy creature's face.

She caressed the lovely creature as she had done all those years ago when she was a child, and when the doe was but a calf. From that time, the adult doe remained with Emily instead of returning to its herd.

It followed her faithfully wherever she went, even at night when she could brave the journey to the family graves at Bolton Priory. As she stood or knelt in prayer, the white doe would stand at her side. The two were inseparable and as she grew older, Emily spent more and more time at Bolton Priory, praying among the stones of the church that Henry's religious upheaval had demolished. And then, in time, Emily also died.

Unlike her brothers and father, she was not buried at Bolton but in Rylstone church at the side of her mother. The faithful doe survived her. It continued to visit the ruins of Bolton Priory where it stood beside the graves of Emily's father and brothers, but in addition it came to Rylstone church every Sunday just as the congregation was leaving. At first, the people did not know why the pure white doe came to visit the church and there was much speculation.

Some thought it was the spirit of the lady who was the benefactor of Bolton Priory, Lady Adeliza or Alice (see Bolton Priory); others believed it was linked to the murder of the Earl of Pembroke because it was often seen to linger near his grave, and yet more thought it was a reincarnation of the Boy of Egremont who is also featured in the story of Bolton Priory.

Wordsworth's lovely poem provides the answer. It was simply the pet doe of Emily Norton, her lifelong friend and companion, and it came to her graveside every Sunday morning for the rest of its life.

24 Semerwater –

The Sunken Village

Semerwater is probably the most beautiful of the natural lakes in Yorkshire and is probably one of the most remote. Some might say that it is rather small to be regarded as a proper lake but that is a matter for conjecture. It is not the largest lake in Yorkshire – that distinction goes to Hornsea Mere in East Yorkshire, now within the county of Humberside, with Malham Tarn in second place. But Semerwater lies third in that league table, being around half a mile long and slightly less than quarter of a mile wide at its widest points. Various older accounts say the water covered an area of around 107 acres but in 1937, the outlet was excavated during efforts to reclaim several acres around the shore, whereupon the level dropped. Although the surface does change due to the influx of water, the lake now covers something like eighty to ninety acres. It is some forty-five feet deep at the deepest part.

It occupies a remote miniature dale off the upper reaches of Wensleydale and can be reached from the A684 between Hawes and Aysgarth. A road leads south from Bainbridge and after a two-mile journey, the shores of Semerwater are revealed. There is a small car park on the water's edge and the lake is popular with anglers, water-skiers and sailing enthusiasts. It is also rich with wildlife and its surrounds offer pleasant walks.

The small communities around the lake have witnessed some historic and strange events; George Fox, the Quaker, was a regular visitor to Countersett and another visitor to the same village was an ancient king whose name has been forgotten with the passage of time. Many writers have come to admire its charms and to record them in their works, one of whom was Sir William Watson who wrote the 'Ballad of Semerwater'.

One curious event occurred at Raydale House which still stands; in 1617, it was besieged by Sir Thomas Metcalfe of Nappa (see Castle Bolton), but the occupants held out against him for two whole days, two being killed and several being wounded in the battle. The owner, called Robinson, was away at the time, and it was his wife and her servants who kept Metcalfe at bay and the siege ended when Mrs Robinson's nephew chanced to arrive from Lancashire. But the records do not give us the reason for this weird battle. There are still Metcalfes in Wensleydale.

The gills, streams, beck and springs of three minor dales provide the water for Semerwater, these being Raydale, Cragdale and Bardale, while two tiny villages lie in the watershed to the south of the lake. These are Stalling Busk and Marsett. To the north is the village of Countersett and beyond is Bainbridge, known for its Roman fort, its stocks and the ancient horn-blowing custom. In bygone times, the horn was blown in the darkness of winter to help travellers find their way through the lonely dales, and today the custom continues.

The present horn was given to the village in 1864 to replace the original which is in a museum at Castle Bolton and it is still blown between the end of September and Shrovetide, described locally as 'between Hawes Back-End Fair and Pancake Tuesday'.

To the east are the heights of Addlebrough (1564 feet) where the Romans once maintained a signalling station. It is said the Druids also used the mountain for their rituals, while the cairn on the summit is said to be more than 3,000 years old. One legend says that a giant, on his way from Skipton to Pendragon Castle near Kirkby Stephen in Westmorland, halted on this summit for a rest. He was carrying a huge chest of gold, and placed this on the ground at his side.

He uttered these words:

'Spite of either God or man,
To Pendragon thou shalt gang.'

And at that instant, a huge hole opened in the mountain top and swallowed the chest of gold. The earth immediately closed over it and there it remains, awaiting the person who can unravel the secret procedures which will recover it. This Pendragon Castle, by the way, has no links with Uther Pendragon who was father of King Arthur.

Lake Semerwater is probably much older than that lofty cairn. Its origins probably date to the Ice Age when glaciers scooped massive quantities of earth from these dales.

Among the larger rocks left behind is the Carlow Stone which stands near the shore of the lake. This, and others around it, have given birth to a legend; it is said they are the result of a stone-throwing contest between the devil and some other fallen angel. The two tired after a while and left their rocks at this place. For years, it was said the Devil's fingerprints could be seen on the Carlow Stone. Another tale is that they formed part of some terrible rites performed by Druids who occupied the remote dales.

The outlet for Semerwater is Britain's shortest river, the Bain, which is only two miles long. It carries the lake's water into the River Ure at Bainbridge for its journey down Wensleydale.

Many thousands of years ago, perhaps during the Iron Age, there was a village on the shores of this lake and indeed, some of the houses might have been lake dwellings built on platforms over the water. But it seems that a sudden flood arose and overwhelmed the flimsy homes, a disaster from which the people never recovered. The existence of that ancient village is a fact, and although some accounts suggest there was also a castle, that is improbable. It was that terrible day, thousands of years ago, when the simple village was flooded, that has given rise to the Legend of Semerwater which continues to be told, albeit in various forms.

In differing accounts of the legend, the lake's name has been given a variety of spellings, including Simmerwater, Seamer Water, Semerwater, Semer Water and even Seamerdale Lake. Today it is known as Semerwater. The origin of this name is obscure, but might come from the

Old English word for 'sea' plus a similar one for mire, meaning marsh.

In bygone times, it might well have been more of a marsh than it is today; that could explain the settlement upon it for lots of lake dwellers built their homes over marshland. When the lake's level was lowered in 1937, some flints and spear-head were found, evidence of the bygone presence of lake dwellings. But an unexpected and serious influx of rainwater both turned the community into a small sea and flooded the dwellings to obliterate them for ever; hence the name and the legend.

There are two main versions of the legend. One tells of a Christian priest, in the earliest days of that faith, travelling to the village in an attempt to convert the local people. They worshipped pagan gods and undertook pagan rituals, and after he had failed to win them to his faith, he put a curse on them – and their village vanished in a flood. It now reclines deep below the waters of this shimmering lake. That is one tale, seldom told now.

The more popular version tells how a poor man, dressed in rags, hungry and cold, trudged along Wensleydale and found himself in a remote village in deepest Raydale.

It was winter and the night was drawing in, so he required food, warmth and, if possible, somewhere cosy and dry to sleep overnight. Some accounts of the legend say that this old man was really one of God's angels in disguise; others do not say who he was, but allow the people to make up their own minds.

At that time, the village was noted for its wealth and style. It had many fine buildings, good roads, rich inhabitants and an abundance of good things. The people, on the other hand, were noted for their lack of charity to others; they were mean almost to the point of cruelty and refused to share their good fortune with any other village, or even with one another. The humble man, who some say bore a venerable appearance, began knocking on doors, asking only for a drink of water. At each splendid house, he met outright hostility and refusal, most of them spitting at him and saying they wanted nothing to do with beggars. Time after time, he was rejected, and then he noticed the priest's house.

The priest was sitting down to his meal and through the window, the stranger could see rich foods like venison and fish, with fresh bread and good wines, and so he knocked on the door. Even the priest rejected him, so he went on towards the castle.

A massive party was in progress with an abundance of food and wine; an ox was being roasted on a spit over a massive log fire in the huge hall and servants were carrying heavy dishes of vegetables and meat to all the guests.

But when the stranger entered, the owner of the castle set his dogs upon him and chased him from the premises. He pleaded with the owner, a black-bearded baron, but it was of no avail, and so he plodded around the quieter streets, knocking on doors, trying the inn and pleading for help. He even asked people in the street if they would give him a drink of water. No one did. All rejected him and many chased him off with dogs or sticks, even though he pleaded with them in the name of Christ.

Eventually, the sun was almost set over the western horizon, he climbed a steep hill out of the village and found a simple cottage on the summit. It was the home of a shepherd and his wife, two poor people who lived from day to day on what they could grow or find locally. It was the most humble of all the dwellings, but he knocked on the door.

It was opened by the shepherd's jolly wife and when he asked for a drink of water, she said, 'Come in and join us. It's cold outside, we have but one loaf of bread in the house and a can of milk, but you are welcome to share them with us.'

The shepherd watched as the stranger hungrily ate some bread and drank the milk, and then he said, 'Look, sir, there is a pile of straw in the corner, the turf fire will burn all night to keep you warm. You can sleep there and tomorrow morning, we shall eat again before you go on your way.'

The weary stranger thanked his new friends and curled up on the straw, falling into a deep sleep within seconds.

The next morning he awoke to find the shepherd had obtained fresh milk and another loaf of bread as well as some meat, and they all sat down to a hearty breakfast before beginning their day. Then the stranger got up to leave.

'You have shared the little you possess,' he said gratefully. 'I am a stranger and you took me in. Blessed be you both, all of your days.'

And then he left. But at first, he did not go far. He climbed the slopes of Addlebrough to look down upon the village. Then he uttered some terrible words.

> 'Semerwater rise! Semerwater sink!
> Swallow all the houses!
> But save the small house where they
> gave me food and drink.'

At his command, the heavens opened and a fearsome storm arose with thunder, lightning and torrential rain. It gathered in all the streams and gills in the three small dales, and cascaded down the mountains until it overwhelmed the village below. The day grew dark and menacing as the waters rose and they never ceased until they had covered the entire village – except the little house on the hill-top where the shepherd lived with his good wife.

Some stories say the old man disappeared from view; others say he was transformed into a glittering angel who was lifted into heaven by unseen hands. But the village and its selfish inhabitants all perished.

For years afterwards, it was said that the roofs of houses, the towers of the castle and the spire of the church could be seen when the water was low, and that the shepherd's cottage was standing even into this century. It was often pointed out with pride, occupying its position on the edge of Lake Semerwater.

Some local people swear the legend is true – after all, doesn't the presence of Semerwater prove it? And it is true that once upon a time, there was a village here.

But who was that mysterious stranger who called to ask for help and was rejected?

That remains a mystery.

25   Sessay –

The Giant of Sessay

After leaving the rugged landscape of Swaledale, the River Swale meanders across the Vale of Mowbray before joining the River Ure near Boroughbridge. This is flat country with none of the grandeur of the Dales, but it does have its places of interest and its links with our distant past.

Among the peaceful, out-of-the-way villages along this part of the Swale's route is Sessay. It is well away from the tourist trail and situated quietly some four miles south of Thirsk. The main London–Edinburgh railway passes to the west while the A19 trunk road from Teeside to York is little over a mile to the east. Nearby at Little Sessay is the school beside the charming little church of St Cuthbert while to the north is Little Hutton, with the bigger village of Hutton Sessay a mile or so away.

There is little to detain the visitor, although St Cuthbert's churchyard boasts an ancient cross, which has been repaired, a lovely lych-gate and some old yews, while the interior contains an interesting brass plaque in the chancel floor. It depicts a famous son of Sessay called Thomas Magnus who was parson here as well as being Archdeacon of the East Riding of Yorkshire. He died in 1550 and the memorial brass shows him wearing a cope with his hands clasped in prayer.

He was the last master of St Leonard's Hospital in York and a legend surrounds his birth. It is said that he was a foundling, having been abandoned by his mother in the church porch. He was found by some tailors who decided to bring up the child, sharing the cost among them all. Thus he became known as Thomas Amang Us which was corrupted to Thomas Magnus. (See Appletreewick for another story about this name). Thomas was a friend of King Henry VIII who made him King's Chaplain and an ambassador, whereupon he was despatched upon several important missions.

Long before his time, however, Sessay was owned by a wealthy family called Darrell, amongst whom was a renowned swordsman who fought in the time of Richard the Lionheart. He was William Darrell and he built a massive house at Sessay, but it was later demolished, Church Farm being built from the stones. The Darrells were powerful and wealthy around the time of Edward II and it is thought they built the first church at Sessay; the current building was constructed during the last century. They presented their church to the Abbey of St Mary at York, but of that early building little has survived. Many years ago, human remains were found in the village, indicating the presence of an old burial ground. A few years ago an ancient stone coffin was used as a horse trough, while a holy water stoup served as a flower pot!

Sessay's part in the folklore of Yorkshire comes from the story of its notorious, ugly and rather ghastly giant.

It is strange that only a mile or so away, another giant dwelt at Dalton (see Dalton). The Sessay monster was a brutish creature, more animal than human, with legs like an elephant's and arms of like size. Its mouth was said to be like that of a lion with fangs like the prongs of a hayfork but it had only one eye. This was in the centre of its forehead and the creature had a permanent expression of anger. It dressed scantily in a vestment of cow-hide which covered its upper body with the hairy side outwards, and over its shoulder, it carried a tree trunk which it used as a massive club.

This horrible giant lived in woods near Sessay and at times, the countryside echoed with its cruel laughter as it achieved yet another successful raid upon the surrounding farms and cottages, or its terrifying growls and snarls if it failed to find food. In its constant search for food, it prowled the district and created untold fear among the villagers.

It consumed huge amounts, especially fat cows and bullocks which it carried off under its arm to eat raw in its cave; it is said the floor was scattered with their bones. If it wanted a change of menu, it would raid one of the local mills to seize a sack of flour or meal, hauling it through the open window before devouring it. Sometimes, it would carry sacks to its cave to make a ghastly gruel of blood and meal.

But its worst offence was to seize young girls at play or babies from their cradles; whenever it failed to find cattle or meal, it would turn to humans for its food.

The people knew from its savage roaring noises whether or not it was on the rampage for human blood and they did their best to protect their children, but they were not always successful. Nothing seemed able to stop the giant.

The villagers did group themselves together in an attempt to kill the creature or at least prevent its wholesale slaughter of innocent children and vital livestock, but they always failed. The sheer sight of the angry giant with its long, blood-stained teeth was enough to terrify most, while a blow from its enormous club would kill the strongest of countrymen.

The poor people of Sessay had reached such a state of fear and worry that there seemed nothing that would put a stop to the giant and its disgraceful activities.

At the time, the manor of Sessay was owned by the powerful Darrell family, of whom Joan was the present survivor. Her father had died, leaving the administration of the huge enterprise to her. She was a capable young woman who had never married, but she was having great difficulty in managing her estate because the giant was always around to frighten her workmen. They refused to tend the fields, to work in the woodlands or to care for the livestock because of their concern about the giant. She was at her wits' end, worrying not only for her own welfare, but for that of her employees and the entire village.

The problem seemed without solution when, as in all good stories, a brave knight appeared on the scene. He was Guy Dawney, the son of Sir John D'Aunay or Dawnay of Cowick Castle in South Yorkshire. He was ancestor of the Dawnay family whose name still appears in inn signs beside the River Ouse and whose present representative is Lord Downe. Guy had been overseas for a long time and was not therefore up-to-date about events in Yorkshire. He did not know, for example, that Joan Darrell's father had died, for as he was passing through Sessay he decided to visit him, Darrell being a good friend of his own father.

When he called at the Darrells' fine mansion, he was invited in by Joan who offered him refreshment. He agreed and so the two met for the first time. None of the accounts suggest that Joan was a beautiful woman; on the contrary, she is depicted as a stern woman, a strong-minded spinster who saw her duty as running the estate as her father would have done. The two spent some time together and it is said that Guy found himself in love with this enigmatic woman. Cynics might say he had his eye on her wealth and vast estates, but in accordance with the romance that is attached to most legends, he fell hopelessly in love with her and asked her to marry him.

He did, however, indicate the practical side of such a marriage, i.e. the merging of two great Yorkshire estates which would be of enormous benefit to any family they might produce. Joan thought about his proposal and gave her answer.

'I will marry you,' she promised. 'But there is one condition.'

'I will fulfil any condition,' he assured her. 'Just you name it, and I will undertake whatever task you impose.'

Joan then told Guy about the rampaging giant who was terrorising the neighbourhood. Guy had not heard the news, partly because of his long absence and partly because his family home was many miles to the south, but as Joan outlined the campaign of terror being waged against the people of Sessay, the bold Guy said he would slay the giant. He hinted he was prepared to die in the attempt, such was his love for Joan.

The deal agreed, they celebrated their pact with a sumptuous meal but even as Guy was drinking the last of his wine, there came a terrible roaring noise outside, and they heard the people screaming. The giant had come to the village and was seeking his prey. From the house, Guy caught sight of the huge creature and was appalled – he was also very worried because he had only his sword as a weapon. It was a puny sword, not the sort that other knights had used for fighting dragons or giants and he must have thought he was facing a hopeless task.

On this occasion, it seems that the giant was not seeking meat, either animal or human, for his dinner, but wanted some sacks of flour from the windmill. As he strode along the village towards the mill, Guy stalked him, sword at the ready.

But the monster towered above him; Guy knew that a thrust of his sword would be little better than a pin-prick upon that tough hide, but if the giant felt even the slightest of pain, he would bring that enormous club crashing down. It would crush Guy like a soft plum. What could he do?

Then the giant reached the windmill and, as was his practice, he simply stooped and thrust his arm through the window to lift out several bags of flour. But at that moment, a gust of wind blew along the river and caused the sails to begin turning. The huge heavy sails began to turn even as the giant was withdrawing his arm and one of them caught him a terrible blow to the head. It knocked him unconscious and he fell to the ground, the entire neighbourhood shuddering with the jolt.

As the monster lay stunned, Guy wasted not one second. With his sword at the ready, he clambered on to the chest of the fallen monster, climbed on to the whiskery face and plunged his sword into that single eye. It was deep enough to reach the brain and with an almighty sigh that blew the leaves off the trees and set the windmill sails whirring, the Giant of Sessay breathed his last.

The village was free. Life could return to normal. And Guy did win the hand of the ambitious Joan and so the two great families and their estates were united. It is said that Sessay has never experienced a more joyful wedding.

26 Thornton Steward –
Kilgrim Bridge

Yorkshire has many villages bearing the name Thornton which, in its earliest form, meant an enclosure surrounded by thorn bushes. Most of the Yorkshire Thorntons are distinguished one from another by a suitable prefix or suffix which provides a further clue to their history or origins. In this case, the village of Thornton Steward dates to pre-Conquest times when it was held by a man called Gospatric; he was succeeded by one called Wymar who was a steward to the Earls of Richmond.

Thornton Steward stands quietly in a neat triangle of land between Leyburn, Masham and Bedale in the lower reaches of Wensleydale and it is well away from the main tourist routes. Set among a network of country lanes, it lies to the north of the River Ure, while opposite, on the southern banks, stand the beautiful ruins of Jervaulx Abbey. The village boasts a neat green, some interesting stone cottages and a village pump. The splendid Danby Hall stands a short distance to the west. This splendid mansion, home of the famous Scropes, has portions dating from the fourteenth century, but the majority is Elizabethan.

Thornton's ancient and tiny church, nearly half a mile along a quiet lane, has origins dating to the time of the Norman Conquest and Saxon remnants can be seen in the fabric of its walls.

There is a bellcote and some other stonework which probably dates to the thirteenth century with other relics of medieval times. If the village has any claim to fame, it is said to be the birthplace of Sir Edward Banks who built both Waterloo Bridge and London Bridge.

But it is another less well known bridge which gives the village its place in the folklore of the Dales. Between Thornton Steward and Jervaulx Abbey, a superb six-arch bridge crosses the River Ure near Kilgram Grange. This is Kilgram Bridge (once known as Kilgrim) and legend says the first bridge across this place was built by the Devil.

The story is a familiar one, both in Yorkshire and elsewhere, and it follows the general pattern by which the Devil, in return for constructing a bridge, demands the life of the first living creature to cross it.

In this case, the villagers had repeatedly built some rather flimsy constructions across the River Ure and each time the river flooded or grew heavy with rain from the fells above, these primitive bridges were washed away. This caused immense problems, especially for farmers bringing home their cattle for milking or their sheep for shearing. It also caused difficulties for the people who had to find an alternative route for their day-to-day outings. A good solid bridge was urgently required and it had to be stout enough to withstand the rigours of the Ure's regular floodwaters.

According to legend, the villagers were approached by the Devil who promised to build a sturdy bridge.

In accordance with his custom, he imposed the usual condition – he demanded the life of the first living creature to cross it. The villagers, desperately in need of a safe, dry and permanent river crossing, agreed to those terms and so a strong bridge was built by Satan. He then awaited his fee – if possible, he wanted a human life, although this was not stipulated.

After the bridge was built, the first to cross the river was a local shepherd but he was an astute man and knew of the requirements demanded by the Devil. So he ordered his obedient sheepdog to sit beside the river while he swam across; once at the other side, he whistled to his dog. It ran across the bridge and became Satan's required victim.

The story says that the dog's name was Grim, and so the bridge became known as Kill Grim Bridge. With the passage of time, that legend has been almost forgotten, and the maps now show the area as Kilgram.

27   Thorpe –

The Cobbler Who Met the Devil

The hamlet of Thorpe is not easily located. I was directed by a stone guidepost almost hidden in the roadside grass, and it bore a black finger pointing into the hills. No distance was indicated. Thorpe lies out of sight along narrow, twisting lanes in a hollow among the foothills of the Pennines. It is situated among an assemblage of curious conical knolls which add mystique to this quiet place. Those hills bear names like Kail Hill, Stebden Hill, Butter Haw Hill, Carden Hill, Skelterton Hill and, perhaps the best known, Elbolton Hill. The latter rises to 348 metres (around 1140 feet) to the immediate west of the village. The smaller Kail Hill is to the immediate east. Thorpe lies concealed among them.

Thorpe, otherwise known as either Thorpe-sub-Montem or Thorpe-in-the-Hollow, is little under two miles to the south east of Grassington via Sheepfold Lathe and it can be reached by car from the Burnsall to Threshfield stretch of the B6160. There are useful footpaths too, one of which leads through beautiful countryside from Burnsall Bridge. The short diversion from the B6160 whether by car or by foot is worthwhile, if only to visit this remote spot to admire the old stone houses and to savour the distinctly rural atmosphere. Motor traffic must often proceed in single lines and one exit warns that the route is unsuitable for motor cars.

The approach lies between high grey stone walls with superb views across Wharfedale towards Linton church, and the village boasts a Georgian manor house. This was gutted by fire in October 1939; the panelling inside was ruined and never replaced, although the rest of the house was beautifully rebuilt.

Time spent here will provide an appreciation of its ancient history: Neolithic herdsmen and hunters lived hereabouts, and there were wild goats, wolves and even wild cattle on the surrounding hills. In more recent times, limestone was quarried nearby and lead was mined from some of the neighbouring landscape.

Another odd aspect of its past is that Thorpe was the home of many cobblers and shoemakers, lots of whom supplied the monks of the surrounding monasteries and abbeys. But why so many cobblers lived and worked in this isolated, tiny place remains a mystery, yet it was still the focus of that craft until the beginning of this century. Even in recent times, Thorpe-crafted shoes were said to be among the finest in the land and craftsmen shoemakers would make long-distance pilgrimages to Thorpe simply to claim they had been to this famous community.

Because of its seclusion, Thorpe was safe from marauders like the Scots and the Danes, and its centuries-old isolation and loneliness might be the reason for its being such a focus of local folklore.

One of the ancient and long-prevailing items of lore is that Elbolton Hill was the haunt of fairies. Indeed, the name means Elves' Hill. Even into this century, the tiny community of Thorpe, only fifty or so in number, firmly believed in the little people.

The villagers were convinced that fairies lived on Elbolton Hill if only because fairy rings continued to appear in the turf. Folk memories continued to persuade them that these were magic rings, and doubtless these naturally expanding circles of fungi helped persuade doubters that the fairies did hold moonlit dances and parties on the slopes and that they did live in fairy caves in and around the hill.

One of those caves is still there. Elbolton Cave lies on the eastern slopes which overlook Thorpe and it is known locally as Navvy Noddle Hole. Centuries ago, primitive people occupied this cave and probably worshipped the sun from one or more of those strange surrounding hilltops. It is not surprising that, in time, the cave was known as the resort of the little people but when the alleged fairy-cave was excavated in 1888, there was an astonishing discovery. Around a long-dead fire in the hearth near the entrance, were the skeletons of twelve men all seated in a curved row, and around them were the bones of animals which no longer roam our land. Those animal remains were tens of thousands of years old, the human skeletons about 2,000 years old, but how had the twelve all died at the same time?

That discovery merely added to the mystical aura of Elves' Hill.

Among the many stories of fairies on Elbolton Hill is the tale of a man from nearby Burnsall who was making his way home one moonlit night. He was a happy fellow who would never harm anyone, let alone the fairies, and as he was walking towards Burnsall he had an unforgettable experience. As he passed the side of Elbolton Hill, in silence, via the footpath which is still there, he was surprised to find a band of fairies enjoying their midnight dancing and having a party. He later described them as being as light as feathers and dressed in green; they had transparent wings and were very agile as they frolicked before him. They had not heard his quiet approach and so he was privileged to witness their revels. He knew he must never disturb the fairies during their activities and so he simply stood and watched at a discreet distance, delighting in their unselfconscious fun and delicate dances. But he forgot himself as each fairy took a turn at entertaining the others. As they performed, he suddenly said, 'I can sing a song if you like ...'

He only wished to join them, to be part of their fun and happiness, but at the sound of his voice, they all panicked and the party became a crowd of terrified little beings. Then, in their fright, they attacked him, throwing stones and physically nipping him as they tried to drive him away.

He tried to brush them off, for although they did not greatly hurt him, he had no wish to harm them. And to his surprise, he caught one. As he brushed them away from his face and clothes, one of them got caught in his large hand and he held on to it, gently but firmly. Then, realising he must show the fairy to his own children at home, he thrust it into his pocket and hurried home with his prize. He was so excited that his return roused his sleeping children and they crowded around as he kept them guessing about the contents of his pocket. Then, when they were suitably fascinated, he said,

'I've got summat here that'll amaze you all … it's a real fairy, I caught him on Elbolton Hill … just you see …'

But as he put his hand inside his pocket, it was empty. The fairy had gone. And none of his children believed him.

Another man who experienced a tough time with the fairies of Elbolton Hill was Daniel Waddilove. He got lost on the slopes one moonlit night and it seems he'd earlier done something to upset or anger the band of little people who lived there. The moment they set eyes upon poor lost Daniel, they began to plague him with tricks and annoyances; the Fairy Queen was in charge and as he tried desperately to find his way home, he found himself led into bogs, into prickly bushes, into nettles and rocky ravines. Unknown creatures bit him on the ankles and he began to think he was hearing shrieks in the night sky, or that he was seeing witches on broomsticks and being confronted by ghosts.

Daniel's terrifying experience continued throughout that night; we might attribute his fears to over-reaction to the frightening situation in which he found himself, being lost in the haunt of the fairies.

There is little doubt that he believed he was being plagued by mischievous fairies led by their Queen and encouraged by no less a sprite than Puck himself. In time, he found the path home and then the Queen came to him and said, 'If you mock us no more, you may go home without further trouble.'

Daniel promised to mend his ways and was promptly filled with admiration for the Fairy Queen, especially her voice which he described as being like the sound of a small, silver trumpet. He said he wished he could hear it again.

Another of the stories associated with this hill is that

whenever the local people were lost in the mists that sometimes enveloped the heights, a mysterious guiding white light would appear ahead of them and lead them to safety. Some said it was held by a mysterious dark figure, and in some areas, a similar light led them through dangerously boggy areas and moorland marshes.

The most enduring folk story to emerge from tiny Thorpe is the story of one of its cobblers. He was Ralph Calvert and he has entered the folk history of the Dales because he met the Devil – and survived without having to agree to any of Satan's conditions.

Indeed, the location and outcome of that meeting can still be seen; this is Dibbles Bridge on the Grassington to Pateley Bridge road (B6265). It is sometimes known as the Devil's Bridge and it crosses the River Dibb after it emerges from Grimwith Reservoir. Steep hills descend on either side as the stone-built bridge crosses this notorious ravine. There are several versions of Ralph's encounter with the Devil and so I will provide one which incorporates most of the known ingredients.

Ralph Calvert was a cobbler who lived in Thorpe. Like many of the others, he depended heavily for his livelihood upon the monks of Fountains Abbey. For them, he made shoes and sandals; he repaired them and also crafted other leather items such as belts or harnesses for their horses.

Ralph was known for the excellence of his work and it was said he could repair three pairs of shoes in the time it took any other cobbler to repair two. He was a small, nimble man and twice a year, just before Christmas and during midsummer, Ralph made the long journey on foot from Thorpe to Fountains Abbey. He took with him the work of the past six months and would receive a further commission for work during the coming six months. It was a good living.

His walk to Fountains took him via Burnsall and Langerton Hill along footpaths which still remain; these led him to the high road. The distance varied between twenty and almost thirty miles, depending upon the route taken.

The shortest route over this rugged landscape was not

always the most speedy. On the high road, there were places of refuge, like the Highwayman's Barn, and refreshment from an old well and water trough which bore the curious inscription: '*Let the horse drink at the spring and thereafter lift his head with joy.*' Upon that road, he travelled along what is now the B6265 to Pateley Bridge and then on to Fountains Abbey.

One day, he walked this way with a sack full of shoes and sandals which he had repaired and upon his arrival at Fountains the monks invited him to stay overnight. He accepted with pleasure. He was wined and dined by his grateful hosts and during the night, experienced a curious dream. He dreamt he met the Devil and struggled with him in a dangerous, deep ravine on the moors, but next morning he dismissed the dream as being due to the rich food he had eaten.

That same morning, having thoroughly enjoyed his overnight stay, he rose early to return to Thorpe, having collected the anticipated sackful of sandals and shoes for repair. He had been paid for work he had done, he had been wined and dined, and so he was very happy and contented as he made his way home across the moors above Pateley Bridge.

But when he reached his usual place for crossing the River Dibb in a deep cleft between the moors, he found the river was swollen with floods and he could not cross. He contemplated wading the raging torrent, but knew it would be dangerous.

He could either wait for the waters to subside or he could go home another way; if he turned off this road at this point, he could walk down the route of the River Dibb to Appletreewick and find his way home from there. It would take him considerably longer; and then he realised that this was remarkably like the place he had seen in last night's dream.

But, being content, he decided to sit down for a while to think about the matter, and in the meantime he would have a snack from the food and drink the kindly monks had packed for his journey. As he sat beside the roaring river, he checked that he was alone, then unpacked his food and began to sing. Although he was not unduly perturbed by his predicament or by his dream, he felt that singing would help his nerves.

He sang a song which begins:

Sing luck a-down, heigh down,
Ho, down derry ...

But to his astonishment, another man joined in and sang the line:

Tol lol derol, darel dol, dol de derry.

Ralph, now more aware than ever of his dream, was surprised to see a tall, well-dressed man at his side. The stranger was gazing at the flooded river. He smiled at Ralph and seemed a very pleasant fellow and so Ralph finished his merry song with the other's accompaniment. Then they discussed the problem of the impassable ford.

The newcomer said it was a long way to Grassington and Ralph commented that he must get back to his wife and family, for they would grow worried about him. Ralph decided that this charming man could never be the Devil and so offered him some of the food he was carrying. The other accepted and sat by his side. Very soon, they were tucking into a splendid feast provided by the monks, and rounded off their meal with some of the abbey's superior wine.

Both were very happy men, even if they were temporarily marooned in the middle of this inhospitable moor. Then, to Ralph's surprise, the man announced that he was in fact Old Nick, otherwise known as the Devil or the Evil One. But Ralph, being unflappable, merely offered the Devil another drink of wine, which was accepted. Thus Ralph befriended the man whom everyone feared and he came to the conclusion that the Devil was a kindly gentleman, not as bad as others claimed.

It also occurred to Ralph that he would have a marvellous tale to tell upon his return to Thorpe, and an even better yarn for the monks of Fountains Abbey, but who would believe him? Who would believe that Ralph Calvert had shared a meal with Old Nick himself beside the roar of the River Dibb in the middle of Greenhow Moor?

Ralph gazed about him. The Devil had started again, and was now tucking into a tasty pie; all around, the curlews were calling and the sheep quietly went about their business of grazing on these desolate heights. There was no one.

'If you are really Old Nick,' said Ralph with some bravado, 'you'll have to prove it!'

'You have been very good to me, a stranger,' said Old Nick. 'You have allowed me to share your food and drink, and for that I am most grateful. If I can prove my identity to you, how would you like me to do so?'

Ralph thought fast and then realised the answer lay before him. There was no bridge across the river – and one was most definitely required.

'If you are Old Nick,' smiled Ralph, 'then build a bridge across this river.'

The man smiled. 'I shall do that for you!' he promised. 'Come back in four days' time, and the bridge will be here.'

The two parted on friendly terms, Ralph taking the route home via Appletreewick, and then he told his story to his wife. She listened in some disbelief, and then told her friends and family. None believed him.

But Mrs Calvert was a persuasive lady and so, on the fourth day, she gathered a crowd of about forty villagers from Thorpe, including the village priest, and they trekked to the crossing-place where Ralph had met the Devil. And there stood a brand new bridge of stone.

The people were amazed and the priest blessed it with holy water, then the villagers erected crosses at each end to safeguard the bridge against any evil that might befall it.

Those crosses remained until the seventeenth century when they were demolished by the Puritans who thought they were too reminiscent of the outlawed Catholic faith.

From that day, the bridge became known as Devil's Bridge, a name it continues to carry even if the maps do show it as Dibbles Bridge. The story is unusual because whenever man has had meetings with the Devil in such circumstances, there was inevitably a condition to be met. Generally, the house or bridge built by Old Nick had to be offered a regular sacrifice to him – the death of some living thing was usually expected once a year, say a cow, a dog, or even a human. But in the case of Dibbles Bridge, no such condition was made.

Sadly, that original stone bridge was not kept in good repair and it became so dangerous that it had to be demolished. Fortunately, the predicament was observed by Sir William Craven (see Appletreewick) and he constructed a new and much improved bridge on the site of the earlier one. But it was still called Devil's Bridge.

The bridge did achieve notoriety in 1975 when a coach from Teeside crashed over the parapet and fell into the ravine below, killing thirty-two lady passengers.

For another folk story involving the cobblers of Thorpe, see the chapter headed 'Burnsall'.

28 Threshfield –

Pam the Fiddler and Our Lady's Well

Wishing-wells and wells dedicated to saints were numerous in the Yorkshire Dales even into the early years of this century and several can still be found. Stories of these wells date to pagan times for it was thought that 'good' spirits lived in them, spirits that kept the people free from disease as well as supplying them with the essential requirement of fresh water.

In medieval times, when nature's water supplies were so often polluted with filth of human and animal waste, it was these amazing springs which were able to deliver an endless supply of clean fresh water which did not cause sickness or disease and so the primitive people thought it was produced by magic. They thought the pure water cured them – in fact, the truth was it simply did not harm them! Thus many wells were regarded as a source of curative water and they were dedicated to saints while others were named in honour of local personalities and some were dedicated to Our Lady. Many had enjoyed this type of status since pagan times, then being dedicated to female pagan deities, usually goddesses or nymphs.

In some cases, the wells were thought to have mystical powers and so the people would pray at them, or honour them in some way, perhaps with floral decorations.

In some cases, it was thought they would grant wishes, consequently, some became wishing-wells.

Of those in the Yorkshire Dales, some are recalled in names like Thor's Well (Thorsgill) or Kettlewell (Ketel's Well), Ketel being a Saxon nobleman, and there were several Lady Wells (Our Lady's Well), St Helen's Wells, St Hilda's Well and St John's Well. Others could be found in villages, such as St Margaret's Well at Burnsall, St Bridget's Well near Ripon and the mysterious St Alkelda's Well at Middleham (see Giggleswick and my book *Murders and Mysteries from the Yorkshire Dales*).

Of these many wells, the one between Threshfield and Grassington has entered the folk history of the Dales because of its association with the ghost of a fiddler and a band of mischievous fairies.

Threshfield is now dominated by large, modern stone houses and lies immediately to the west of Grassington, the two communities being separated only by the imposing Grassington Bridge and the River Wharfe. Some insist that this bridge is correctly named Linton Bridge, Linton being another nearby village. The older part of Threshfield lies on top of the hill and has several beautiful old houses and an area known as The Park which was formerly the village green; it had its own set of stocks.

Some distance beyond the village boundary is another superb old building which is now a primary school. It stands beside the road from Linton Falls to Grassington Bridge.

This is the former Free Grammar School, many of whose pupils have achieved national distinction; one of them was Dr Thomas Whitaker, the topographer and historian whose history of this region contained thirty-two plates of Yorkshire scenes by the landscape artist Turner (Joseph Mallord William Turner, 1775-1851). These were some of Turner's earliest drawings.

This beautiful old building has mullioned windows and a distinctive porch with a small room above. This was once the abode of the headmaster. The school is said to be haunted by the ghost of Pam the Fiddler who once terrified the teachers and who was said, from time to time, to play for the pupils or to terrify passers by. The school, which lost its status as a grammar school in 1870 to become the village elementary school, was founded in 1674 by Matthew Hewitt, the rector of Linton. His family built several of the splendid stone houses around the village green, including Park Grange (1640).

For a brief period, Threshfield was known for a particular type of industry – besom manufacture. This was introduced by a family called Ibbotson who settled at Ling Hall (since rebuilt) and they made their famous besoms from heather twigs. These were sold across a wide area of these Dales. It is said that the trade was brought here by a Scottish cattleman and drover who arrived in the middle of the seventeenth century and built himself a fine stone house. He remained here and his descendants, the Ibbotsons, made their name famous through their besoms.

Another of their claims to fame was that, some 190 years ago, they owned a horse called Pigeon which, over a period of ten years, was never beaten in a race. One of Pigeon's shoes was preserved on a stable door at the rebuilt Ling Hall. The Ibbotsons became noted horse-dealers and supplied ponies for another of Threshfield's unlikely industries, coal-mining. Threshfield Colliery used to occupy a site of the moors above until its useful life was ended by floodwater. The locally named Jagger ponies would carry coal to Pateley Bridge, the procession being led by a piebald pony decorated with ribbons and bells. At night, the bells heralded the arrival of this long procession.

As you travel from Grassington over the bridge and turn left, there is a flight of steps down to an ancient well beside the River Wharfe. This is variously known as Linton Well, Threshfield Well, Our Lady's Well or just the Lady Well. Following this road, past the old school noted above, is the village of Linton, a small but important village which boasts three different styles of bridge and a ford across the beck. There is a modern road bridge, a narrow pack-horse bridge and a clapper bridge on piers made of local boulders.

Linton's ancient church, which is the parish church for the larger Grassington as well as for Threshfield and Linton (see Grassington) stands some distance away beside the river, and Lile Emily's Bridge can be also seen at Linton (see Rylstone).

Linton's white-walled Fontaine Inn is named after yet another Dalesman who left this remote area to make his fortune in London. This was Richard Fontaine who became an alderman of the city of London in 1721 and who built an almshouse in Linton for six poor men and women. Even today, it is known as the Fontaine Hospital as it overlooks the green near the clapper bridge. It was designed by Sir John Vanbrugh, the designer of Castle Howard in Yorkshire's Ryedale.

One recent past resident of Linton was the famous Dales writer, Halliwell Sutcliffe, whose classic book *The Striding Dales* (1929) did so much to capture the romance of the Dales. He lived here at the house known as White Abbey and his stories remain as fresh as ever.

It was Sutcliffe who chronicled the story of Pam the Fiddler and some say that he elaborated upon existing folk tales, adding figments of his own imagination to expand and strengthen existing tales. But in that change lies the power of folk stories – they are altered and expanded with the passing of time and remain fresh through constant re-telling.

Sutcliffe gives an account of the holy wells of the Dales, but in his story of Our Lady's Well at Threshfield, he links it to the famous ghost of Pam the Fiddler which, he said, once assaulted a Grassington tinker near the school. Some other accounts do not associate Pam the Fiddler with Our Lady's Well, although some do recount the sighting of an unidentified ghost as part of the ancient tale.

However, in his *Yorkshire Legends and Traditions* (1888), the Revd Thomas Parkinson does associate Pam the Fiddler with the imps of Our Lady's Well, referring to Pam as 'the Threshfield ghost'. His source was a Dr Dixon who had earlier written *Stories of the Craven Dales*. According to Sutcliffe, an early headmaster of the Free Grammar School used to entertain his pupils by playing the fiddle and he became known as Pam the Fiddler. He would play his fiddle on the fells too, or by the riverside. When folk were out at night, they would often hear the musical strains of his pleasant work. He could play music which made their feet wish to dance, as well as traditional airs and romantic tunes.

In time, he was asked to venture out of his village to play at local fairs, weddings and parties. But in some cases, he was plied with too much ale and he would occasionally return to his home at the school having drunk more than was wise, but he always played his fiddle even when in this merry condition. Then one moonlit night, after a jolly party, Pam came home late and sat in the playground to play. The music was dreamlike and beautiful, but neither his playing nor Pam's merry condition pleased the rector who chanced to be passing. He was an austere character without any sense of humour and devoid of all sense of genuine pleasure, and when he heard Pam playing by the light of the moon he marched across the schoolyard and seized the violin to halt the music. He then started to lecture Pam about his inebriated condition.

Pam remonstrated and tried to recover his precious fiddle, but the tussle rapidly developed into a tough fight. Small and wiry though he was, Pam was no match for the burly vicar and soon he lay crumpled on the ground. The vicar was horrified – he checked to see whether Pam was feigning death or injury, but the terrible result of his action was clear. He had killed Pam the Fiddler. He went home for a pickaxe and spade, and by the light of the moon, buried Pam close to the school. The vicar's conscience claimed it was a fair fight and he convinced himself that he had never intended to kill the schoolmaster, and so he said a prayer over the grave and undertook the secret burial of his victim.

It was claimed that, for years afterwards, the ghostly strains of a violin could be heard by those who walked past the school at night. Even in modern times, it is said that passing Dalesmen have been frightened by the distant sound of a violin or the sight of a ghost.

Quite surprisingly, there was another violin-player in the village. When a new rector arrived in 1742, it was soon learned that he had a peculiar ambition – he wished to be the finest ballroom dancer there had ever been and he would practise his steps before a mirror, sometimes even travelling to France to learn new steps and develop his skills. He was the Revd Benjamin Smith who was a nephew of Sir Isaac Newton. He secured the services of a local fiddler to provide the music for his dancing.

It was a condition of his playing that he must always

have his back to the rector, so as never to see him in action as he rehearsed and practised his intricate steps. It is said that on one occasion, this fiddler dared to look over his shoulder at the dancing parson, but his action was noted and he was thrown out of the room, fiddle and all. But I know of no links between this fiddler and Pam the Fiddler.

One of the enduring folk stories of this region is the tale of a man staggering home to Threshfield after a rather late drinking-session in one of the local inns. As he approached the village, he came upon a sight rarely seen by other mortals – it was the ghostly figure of Pam the Fiddler playing his music to a troup of dancing imps and fairies.

The wayfarer was not too drunk to realise the uniqueness of his sighting and so he stood in silence to watch these late-night revels. But something tickled his nose and although he tried to avoid it, he broke into a fit of sneezing. This made the dancers realise that they had been spied upon and they gave chase because the wayfarer ran for his life. He knew there was only one refuge from the angry fairyfolk that followed him – and that was Our Lady's Well. Throughout the district, it was known as a refuge from boggarts, imps, devils, goblins, witches and other unsavoury creatures. As the angry imps chased him, he ran for his life and managed to reach the well before his pursuers.

He leapt in and remained up to his neck in the cold water as the angry imps rampaged around the rim, unable to reach him to execute their punishment. And so he remained until sunrise. When the sun rose and the cocks crowed, the angry mob of fairies had to disperse, but not before they had warned him of dire dangers if ever he trespassed upon their parties or privacy in the future. When they had gone, the now very sober wayfarer climbed out of the well and made his dripping way home, albeit secure in the knowledge that he had defeated the legendary imps. It is said he was no worse for his long immersion in the cool waters of the well.

For years afterwards, Our Lady's Well was regarded as a place of refuge from the troubles that life can throw at us.

29   Thrybergh –

St Leonard's Cross

Thrybergh is a mining-village between Rotherham and Doncaster in South Yorkshire. It is well away from the district traditionally associated with the Dales, being surrounded by industry, and yet it has Saxon origins as the name suggests. For centuries, noble families have occupied the mansion in Thrybergh Park on a hill above the village and one of the holders of that land was the Reresby family.

One of them, Sir John, was born here in 1634 and he was a great supporter of the royalist cause. He produced a popular idea in which all the houses in London should be taxed because the capital was attracting too many workers from the rest of the country. He felt this would dissuade people moving into London at the expense of the provinces. Sir John had five sons and four daughters, but the eldest, William, the heir to the great estates, was a gambler and lost the entire family fortune and estate during a single cockfight. He bet on the wrong bird and died, in debt, in Fleet Prison and so the last of the Reresbys occupied the fine house at Thrybergh. They left in 1689 after living there since the fourteenth century.

The village church also dates to the fourteenth and fifteenth centuries and contains some interesting stained-glass windows, while eight children are shown on one monument dated 1818. It is to the memory of the wife of John Fullerton whose family subsequently occupied Thrybergh Park.

The remains of two old crosses are of interest. One is in

the churchyard and depicts a man with a book, and the other is in a field off a lane near the church. Although incomplete, the latter is known as St Leonard's Cross and it is the reminder of a powerful love story. It involved a member of the Reresby family, Sir Leonard de Reresby.

Although the cross is known as St Leonard's, its correct name might be *Sir* Leonard's Cross as Leonard does not appear upon the list of canonised English saints. But it is a small point, and Sir Leonard was undoubtedly a good man. He lived during the time of the Crusades and was a very devout and holy man, a truly sincere person who spent a lot of his time at Mass and in prayer. He also felt a deep sense of duty to his country. He had met his beloved wife near the stone cross in a field near the church, and their romance had been conducted during regular visits to the old cross; by both, it was held in special affection. They married at the little church and were an ideal couple.

Sir Leonard was a fine soldier, an expert horseman, powerful sword-fighter and capable bowman and although he had a lovely home, a beautiful wife and a very comfortable way of life, his sense of national duty led him to believe that he should be helping to fight in the Crusades. He prayed for guidance, asking God to help him make the right decision.

That decision meant he had to leave his wife and his country temporarily because he went off to fight the Saracens. As his wife watched him ride away, she must have wondered if she would ever see him again.

She was wealthy in her own right, being heiress of the Normanvilles who owned Thrybergh Park before the Reresbys, and she was a good woman, faithful and true. But Leonard had the misfortune to be captured by the warring Saracens and he was placed in prison where he was not allowed to communicate with anyone, especially anyone from home. He talked with no other knights; he had no visitors and could not get a message back to his wife in Thrybergh. He tried to find a wandering minstrel, a travelling merchant, a home-going knight – anyone who might take a message to his waiting wife, but none came. He was in prison for almost seven years, during which time no message ever reached home.

Meanwhile, back at Thrybergh, a handsome young Lord had noticed the fair girl who awaited her knight from the Holy Land and he began to court her. She explained that she was married and that she would never be unfaithful to her husband, even though she had not had word from him for more than six years. She guessed he was in prison – why else would he not contact her? There was no word to say he had been killed in action and his love for her, and his sincere nature, would never let him wilfully desert her. She had total faith in him, even after all that time.

But as the months crept by, her new suitor pointed out that if she had not heard from him within seven years, it could be presumed that he had died. Then they could marry. He tried to convince her that Leonard had died – why else would he not contact her? He could have died on the battlefield … So persuasive was he, that she agreed to think again if she had not heard from Leonard within the seven years.

She promised that if Leonard had not returned or given word by the seventh anniversary of his departure to the Crusades, then she would marry her new suitor. And so the time crept by, month after month, with two people watching the passing of the days in Thrybergh, and Leonard sitting alone in his cell in Palestine, unable to contact anyone.

But he had not been idle. He had marked on the walls of his cell the passing days and was horrified when he realised he had been incarcerated for almost seven years. He knew of the rule by which a man could be declared dead; his wife was still a young woman, she was still very attractive and she was an heiress as well. She might fall prey to some unscrupulous fellow.

He knew he could not escape by mortal means; he had tried again and again. He knew he had to rely totally on the power of prayer. In those desperate moments, he prayed as he had never prayed before, relying on all his deep reserves of faith in his God and then, as if by a miracle, an opportunity arose. He could not let this chance pass without acting.

His warder's back was turned for the briefest of moments, but it was enough for Sir Leonard de Reresby.

He sneaked out of the gaol, disguised himself with some clothes he found in a cupboard, stole a horse and began the long ride home. He still wore the shackles on his wrists and wasted no time trying to remove them. Over night and day he galloped towards the sea, taking a cargo boat and finally entering England, thin, starved and almost a wreck. It was as if a hidden power was guiding him and giving him strength to continue.

He knew he could not rest – he could have sent a message, but decided he could reach Thrybergh before any messenger, however swift. He rode on and on. But on the morning of the anniversary of his departure, his wife, believing herself to be a widow, was to be married and the wedding party had already assembled. As she was driven towards the church in her brideswain, she decided to stop and visit the cross where she and Leonard had met. It had always meant so much to her.

And as she entered the field, there, crawling across the grass on his hands and knees, his wrists still shackled, his face gaunt and dirty, his clothing in tatters and his body thin through lack of food, was Sir Leonard. In spite of his condition, she recognised him. He had arrived just in time and was but a few yards from the church. Thus he prevented the marriage of his wife and, according to the legend, they lived happily ever after and became popular and long-standing Lords of Thrybergh. That old cross still marks that romantic place.

30 Walton –

The Walton Calves

From time to time, the silly or simple actions of a few people can be commemorated down the centuries in folk stories such as the Austwick Carles (see Austwick). A similar fate has affected Walton.

This Walton is near Wetherby and although it lies close to the River Wharfe, it is situated in the flat Vale of York rather than the hills of the Pennines. It should not, however, be confused with another Walton near Wakefield which was the home of a most eccentric naturalist called Charles Waterton.

The Walton in our story is a quiet place, well off the beaten track, although it does have a long history dating to Roman times. A Roman road called Rudgate passed nearby and there was a ford in Walton which became known as Helen's Ford, named after Helena, the mother of Constantine the Great. The historian Dodsworth believed this ford to be near the site of a Roman station called *Calcaria*, and in fact the remains of several Roman stations have been discovered nearby.

The village has Celtic associations too and now contains several seventeenth-century buildings – at the turn of this century, many were thatched and the community was regarded as very rural and very peaceful. There was once a chapel here with a well nearby, but both have long disappeared.

The flow from a spring in the village was said to cure eye ailments and also to act as a good-luck charm for lovers who drank its waters.

Walton's church dates back some six hundred years, and its slim tower boasts a Norman base while much of the building can be traced to the fifteenth century. There is a Jacobean font and in the chancel can be seen the tomb of an armour-clad knight of the fourteenth century. One of the famous sons of Walton was the hymn-writer Robert Fairfax, a member of the famous Fairfax family who lived nearby at The Old Hall and who were so prominent during the Civil War. This Fairfax was a peaceful man who composed Masses which continue to be heard in churches throughout the country and even across the world, and he wrote the anthems used to commemorate the accession of Henry VII during whose reign he lived and worked.

It was the Walton well which attracted the people and it could be seen even into the early years of this century. The local people would gather around it, especially the young ones for whom it became a meeting-place. Some would tie ribbons or strips of cloth and rags around the well to commemorate their visit or perhaps to remind them of a romance or happy event nearby. For this reason, it became known as the rag well.

Then one day, the notorious but well-loved highway-man Swift Nick Nevison came to drink at the well and, being tired, he settled down for a nap.

Some of the local youths saw him and recognised him, and as there was a reward for his capture, they decided to inform the authorities. They went off to find the constable, but he was nowhere to be found and so the lads decided to carry out their own arrest. They would seize the highwayman and lock him in a secure building until they could notify the right person. But as they crept forward to catch hold of Nevison, he awoke and quickly realised his predicament.

He pointed a stick at them, pretending that it was a gun, and this so terrified them that they all ran away. Nevison avoided capture and hurriedly left Walton.

For their cowardice and stupidity in thinking the stick was a gun, those men of Walton became known as Walton Calves, a name used by those of neighbouring villages who wish to annoy or embarrass the Walton menfolk.

31   Wortley –

The Dragon of Wantley

The Yorkshire Dales do not possess a wealth of legends associated with dragons. In fact, this is the only one which has come to my notice and it is not entirely what it seems!

Conversely, there are several dragon legends in the nearby North York Moors which lie to the east of the county, and yet more further north in County Durham (see my *Folk Tales From the North York Moors*), but all have similarities. Almost without exception, they tell of a brave knight who had to destroy a dragon, sometimes known as a worm, and who equipped himself with a special suit of armour studded with knife blades. In all cases, the knight wins, sometimes against overwhelming odds, and quite often he is rewarded with the hand of a lovely maiden which, in some of the tales, he has rescued. Most, if not all, these yarns are local variations on the theme of St George and the Dragon, or Good versus Evil.

In the case of the Dragon of Wantley, it seems the story is not a genuine legend whose origins are lost in the mists of time. It seems to have been especially created, albeit some time ago, as a form of criticism of events which occurred in and around Wortley and some authorities believe it is nothing more than a satire based on several dragon tales.

Nonetheless, it has become a Dales legend in its own right and although Wortley is beyond the area generally described as the Yorkshire Dales, it does lie in South Yorkshire and the story of its dragon is therefore worthy of inclusion in this book.

Situated in the industrial belt of South Yorkshire some six miles from Rotherham, Wortley is not on the tourist trail but it does have a history stretching back to Roman times; they had iron-mines here. It overlooks the River Don and has some splendid views over the crags of Wharncliffe Chase which is the setting for the legend. Within those woods is the Dragon's Den. Sir Walter Scott came here too, and based the opening scenes of Ivanhoe upon Wharncliffe Chase. These are his opening words:

In that pleasant district of merry England which is watered by the River Don, there extended in ancient times a large forest, covering the greater part of the beautiful hills and valleys which lie between Sheffield and the pleasant town of Doncaster. The remains of this extensive wood are still to be seen at the noble seats of Wentworth, of Warncliffe (sic) Park and around Rotherham. Here haunted of yore the famous Dragon of Wantley ...

The church, in which one legend said Dick Turpin was buried (he is buried in York!), boasts a fourteenth-century window and there is some artwork by a member of the Wortley family, Archibald Stuart-Wortley.

He was the first president of the Society of Portrait Painters.

Close to the church is Wortley Hall, the home of the Wortley family, the Earls of Wharncliffe. They have occupied this home since the time of William the Conqueror, but the name of the dragon is a corruption of their name, Wantley being a local name for Wharncliffe.

One of the most famous Wortleys was Sir Thomas who loved shooting his bow and arrow and hunting with hounds. An old account says he was 'much given to showtinge in the longe bowe and had much delite in huntinge'. In 1510, he built a hunting-lodge on a high spot in Wharncliffe Chase and for years it bore an inscription which read:

Pray for the saule of Thomas Wryttelay, Knyght, for the kyngys bode to Edward the forthe Rychard therd Hare the VII and Hare VIII hows saules God perdon wyche Thomas cawsyd a loge to be made hon this crag ne mydys of Wancliffe for his plesor to her the hartes bel in the yere of our Lord a thousand cccc x.

So renowned were Thomas' hunting hounds that he

received requests for pups from far and near, the King of Scotland being among those who sought them. It seems he spent most of his time in the hunting-lodge he had constructed, but there is one cruel story about him – it is said he destroyed an entire village so that he could improve the famous Chase, but the act drove him demented and the local people regarded that as an adequate punishment from God.

Another tyrannical act was undertaken by Sir Francis Wortley and it is claimed that this gave rise to the dragon legend. The incident arose during the reign of Elizabeth I from a legal dispute between a Mr Nicholas Wortley and the local people; Wortley was pressing the rector of Penistone over the payment of some tithes. It seems the residents paid their tithes to the church who in turn passed the payment to the estate of the Wortleys or Wharncliffes. It seems the matter was never resolved by Mr Nicholas Wortley, but when Sir Francis succeeded him, he decided to determine the affair in what was later described as a tyrannical and oppressive manner. This caused a great wave of anger among the local people who sought someone to fight on their behalf – they needed a champion to fight the oppressor.

According to one account, they selected a gentleman of quality who lived at the other side of the River Don; in fact, his mansion, called More Hall, overlooked Wharncliffe Chase and belonged to a family called More. At the time of this dispute, according to one account, the resident of More Hall was a Mr Blount who had married an heiress of the More family, and he might have become, in legend, the brave knight who fought the dragon. The dragon, of course, alluded to the Wortleys/Wharncliffes. Another account says the champion was a Mr Lyonel Rowlestone who married the widow of Francis Bosville, whose three orphan children were robbed of their rightful inheritance.

In that case, the parishioners all joined in opposition to the Wortleys and a parchment agreement was drawn up in the reign of James I, naming all the participants. One of them was called Wordsworth, a distant ancestor of the poet. Yet another story says the dispute was really one between the Mores and the Wortleys, and it is perhaps of significance that the family crest of the Mores did contain a green dragon. Sir Walter Scott wondered if the animal should really have been a wolf or some other destructive creature, but for all the speculation, the story of the Dragon of Wantley lives on.

In its original form, it was told entirely in verse and it does have a very humorous, even mischievous, slant. It was produced as an opera in 1738 by Henry Carey, and in 1873, the artist Sir Edward J. Poynter (1836-1919) exhibited, at the Royal Academy, a painting entitled 'More of More Hall and the Dragon'. In spite of its durability, the author of the original story is unknown.

This is his description of the dragon:

This dragon had two furious wings,
Each one upon each shoulder,
With a sting in his tail as long as a flail,
Which made him bolder and bolder.
He had long claws, and in his jaws
Four and forty teeth of iron;
With a hide as tough as any buff
Which did him round environ.

Unlike many others, this dragon had wings and we are told that it ate trees, houses, poultry, farmyard stock and even rocks, and that it once consumed three children at one meal. It breathed fire too, and was so dangerous that no man or the bravest of knights dared approach it. But the people learned of a great and powerful knight called More of More Hall. He was so strong he had once picked up a horse and swung it around by its tail until it was dead, simply because it had annoyed him. Then he had eaten the horse, all except the head. By all accounts, he was the right man to dispose of the dragon.

Off he went to Sheffield to obtain a suit of armour made from that city's finest steel, and he asked that it be studded with six-inch spikes. Even the toes of his boots were spiked and, having discovered he could secure the right armour, More set about his task. The people were overjoyed and offered him all their wealth and goods if he could dispose of the dragon, but he declined. All he wanted, he said, was one sixteen-year-old girl, with snow-white skin, blushing cheeks and black hair, to anoint him all over with oil the night before his battle, and to dress him in the morning. It seemed an odd request, but he found a willing maid because he dressed in his armour and sallied forth. The verse says:

> He frighted all, cats, dogs and all,
> Each cow, each horse, and each hog
> For fear they did flee, for they took him to be,
> Some strange outlandish hedgehog.

It seems that More had decided that brains might be better than brawn in his forthcoming tussle, and he decided to outwit the dragon. He did so by hiding down the village well, for he knew the dragon came here to drink. As the verse says:

> It is not strength that always wins,
> for wit doth strength excel;
> which made our cunning champion
> creep down into a well.

When the dragon poked its head into the well to take its drink, our champion smote it on the nose and shouted 'Boo' at it, but the dragon merely lifted him out and demanded a fair fight. And so they fought for two whole days, each avoiding the more dangerous attacks by the other, and at the end of two days, neither had suffered even one minor wound.

This boring fight wore on and on until the dragon suddenly lashed out with a blow which sent the champion reeling, and then he rushed at More intending to throw him into the air like a ball. But More lashed out with his spiked boot and, probably by very good fortune, managed to inflict a serious wound to the dragon's spine. It hit a vital spot, the only place upon its entire body where such a wound would prove fatal and so it did. The dragon sank to the ground, dying. The final verse says:

'Oh', quoth the dragon, with a deep sigh,
And turned six times together,
Sobbing and tearing, cursing and swearing,
Out of its throat of leather.
'More of More Hall! O, thou rascal,
Would I had seen thee never;
With the thing on your foot, thou has pricked my gut
And I'm quite undone for ever!
Murder, murder!' the dragon cried,
'Alack, alack for grief!
Had you but missed that place, you could
Have done me no mischief.'
Then his head he shaked, trembled and quaked,
And down he lay and cried,
First on one knee, then on back tumbled he,
So groaned, kicked, shat and died.

Thus the people of Wharncliffe triumphed over the dragon which had tormented them, and their success, however bizarre, has entered the folklore of the Yorkshire Dales.